Y0-ABR-448

TIN HOUSE
M A G A Z I N E

*She was calling to say goodbye. There was really
only one thing for her to say, those three words
that all the terrible art, the worst pop songs and
movies, the most seductive lies, can somehow
never cheapen. I love you.*

*She said it over and again before the line went dead.
And that is what they were all saying down their
phones, from the hijacked planes and the burning
towers. There is only love, and then oblivion. Love
was all they had to set against the hatred of
their murderers.*

—Ian McEwan

Volume Three · Number Two

Tin House is pleased to announce
the Second Annual SUMMER LITERARY SEMINARS
in **St. Petersburg, Russia**, Fiction and Poetry Contest.

First prize in each category is plane fare, accommodations, and tuition to SLS St. Petersburg 2002 AND publication in *Tin House*. Second prize in each category is free tuition to SLS 2002, and third prize winners receive partial tuition scholarships. Initial judges include past and present SLS faculty and current *Tin House* editors. Final Judge in fiction: Padgett Powell. Final Judge in poetry: Michael Burkard.

SLS in St. Petersburg is a two- or four-week (contest awards are for the entire four weeks) jaunt to one of the most literary cities in the world with an array of American and Russian writers. This year's faculty includes: Aimee Bender, Robert Creeley, Arkadii Dragomoschenko, Dave Eggers, Mikhail Iampolski, Mary Karr, Colm McCann, Josip Novakovich, Robert Olmstead, Padgett Powell, Mark Richard, Jerome Rothenberg, Rob Spillman, and many others to be announced. Workshops are offered in fiction, poetry, nonfiction, playwriting, and hypertext in addition to Russian literature seminars and lectures. For further information see the SLS website at http://www.sumlitsem.org.

Contestants who are not already subscribers to *Tin House* are eligible for $5 discount on a year's subscription. Vouchers will be mailed out to all who enter the SLS contest.

To enter in prose, submit one short story or novel excerpt (no more than 25 pages). Poetry submissions may include 1-3 poems. Each entry must arrive with a $10 reading fee. Multiple entries require multiple reading fees. Make checks payable to Summer Literary Seminars. Deadline: March 15, 2002. Winners will be announced on the SLS website by April 15.

Mail submissions to:
Fiction/Poetry Contest
Summer Literary Seminars
P.O. Box 1358
Schenectady, NY 12301

"The answers are never what you'd expect."*

Almost

Elizabeth Benedict

"*Almost* is the most engrossing novel I've come across in a long time . . . I don't know what to compare it to—except life."
—Jeff Giles, *Newsweek*

"There are mysteries galore to be solved in *Almost*, some obvious and some less so. It is to Benedict's credit that she refuses to answer some of the most pressing questions—for the reader or for Sophy. Why do we love whom we love? And why do we stop loving them? As Benedict makes clear, the answers are never what you'd expect."
—Karen Karbo, *New York Times Book Review**

"Benedict's ability to write with poignant humor of life's leftovers is what gives *Almost* its charm—that and the fact that she is a flawless writer who doesn't waste her words."
—Susan Dooley, *Washington Post Book World*

"The great life of this book arises out of Benedict's judicious and sometimes startling mastery of language. The casual dialogue here and the descriptions of the ordinary remind me of Raymond Carver's short stories and poems. Nothing phony, nothing literary, nothing done, at least so you'd notice, for effect."
—Maureen Corrigan, *Fresh Air* (NPR)

HOUGHTON MIFFLIN COMPANY

www.houghtonmifflin.com
wherever book are sold

Editor-in-Chief/Publisher
WIN McCORMACK

Consulting Editor for the Music Issue
RICK MOODY

Editor
ROB SPILLMAN

Managing Editor
HOLLY MACARTHUR

Poetry Editor
AMY BARTLETT

Senior Editor
JEANNE McCULLOCH

Assistant Editors
CHRISTINA CHIU
SERENA CRAWFORD
MICHELLE WILDGEN

Editor-at-Large
ELISSA SCHAPPELL

Art Director
BILL STANTON

Readers
ALLISON DUBINSKY
GABRIELE HAYDEN
KATE NOSON
JILL OWENS
MONTANA WOJCZUK

Interns
CORDELIA LEMBO
LISA SPERANSKY
NICK TORREY

Contributing Editors
AGHA SHAHID ALI
DOROTHY ALLISON
ALBERTO FUGUET
TUCKER MALARKEY
CHRISTOPHER MERRILL
RICK MOODY
RACHEL RESNICK
HELEN SCHULMAN
TOM SPANBAUER
IRVINE WELSH

Copy Editor
GREG VILLEPIQUE

Proofreaders
MARGARET DAVIS
ALLISON DUBINSKY

Tin House is published quarterly by McCormack Communications. Vol. 3, No. 2, Winter 2002. Printed by Edwards Brothers, Ann Arbor, MI. Send submissions (with SASE) to: PO Box 10500, Portland, OR 97296-0500. ©2002 McCormack Communications LLC. All rights reserved. Neither this publication nor any part of it may be reproduced, stored in a retrieval system, or transmitted in any form or by any means, electronic, mechanical, photocopying, recording or otherwise, without the prior written permission of McCormack Communications LLC. Visit our website at www.tinhouse.com. ISBN# 0-9673846-9-9.

Subscription Service: Basic subscription price: 1 year $59.80. Send subscription requests, inquiries, and change of address to PO Box 469049, Escondido, CA 92046-9049, or e-mail to tinhouse@pcspublink.com., or call 1-800-786-3424.

Newstand distribution through Big Top Newsstand Services. (www.indypress.org) For more information, please call (415) 643-0161, fax (415) 643-2983, or e-mail info@bigtoppubs.com.

Volume Three   **Number Two**

Winter 2002

FICTION

NEW VOICES

POETRY

POETRY

FEATURES

Winter 2002

FEATURES

INTERVIEW

LOST AND FOUND

Winter 2002

LOST AND FOUND

THE LAST WORD

Winter 2002

EDITORS' NOTE

This issue went into production before the tragedy of September 11 and was shipped to the printer several weeks afterwards. Like everyone else, we were totally devastated by the disaster. Our first response was to think that the Music Issue now seemed unimportant in the scheme of things. But as we sat around listening to a mix of Leonard Cohen, Chemical Brothers, Bob Dylan, and Beethoven quartets, we quickly realized that now more than ever we need music—and good writing about great music. When the going gets tough, the tough break out their bongos.

We were aided considerably by contributing editor Rick Moody, who sat in as consulting editor for the Music Issue. In addition to being one of our nation's finest writers, Rick plays guitar, sings, and writes songs, and does an eerie Dylan imitation. We are extremely grateful for his knowledge, vision, and patience. In addition to his consulting and editing, he also wrote about his collaboration with longtime hero Meredith Monk. We hold our lighters high in appreciation and celebration.

Our aim was to put together a music issue that would spin expectations. From the opening pages, we feature fresh, original voices and ideas, such as new voice A. J. Albany's "Low Down," a raw portrait of growing up in the grungy glam 60s jazz and junkie world. Both Geoffrey O'Brien and David Grubbs take on silence in their essays, while Francine Prose interviews sax prodigy Leon Michels (who happens to be her son). Jonathan Lethem, grandmaster flash of reinventing clichéd forms—the Western, the Noir detective novel—re-imagines the liner note. Ronald "Stozo" Edwards, legendary illustrator of George Clinton's Funkadelic album covers, does a crazy duet with poet Thomas Sayers Ellis, and the results are nothing short of boogielicious.

So go grab your bongos, put on *One Nation Under a Groove*, and get funky.

New Voice

by A. J. ALBANY

LOW DOWN

OE ALBANY was a great jazz pianist. That was the opinion of Charlie Parker, Lester Young and scores of other musicians who played with him. I too was in awe of his talent, but I also loved him all out of proportion, as only a daughter can. He was born in Atlantic City, 1924, and died in New York City, 1988, broke and blind, his body destroyed from a half-century of addictions and sadness. In one of his last letters to me, he warned: "Watch out for Old Lady Life—she can be an evil bitch." His life and career have been pretty well documented, but there has always been an absence of information regarding his whereabouts in the sixties. This was the decade when I knew him best—if he wasn't in jail or rehab, we were together. This is my account of our lives during that time—some of it was told to me by my father, but most of it is from my own fragmented memory.

Growing Up Amid Jazz Stars, Junkies and Other Freaks of Nature

Mother and daughter (two weeks old), 1962

My parents met in 1959 at one of Erroll Garner's parties. Dad and Erroll were pretty close, and when I was born, he asked to be my godfather, but some Italian guy named Frank Perry was already in place for that position. I have a favorite picture of myself on top of Mr. Garner's shoulders. He was a very kind and gentle man. My mother, Sheila Boucher, walks into the party, and someone lets her know that Joe Albany is at the piano, which sets her bohemian heart aflutter, since her favorite album at the time is *The Right Combination*. Funny to think of jazz musicians generating that sort of rock-star excitement among women. She makes her way over to the piano and introduces herself as an aspiring jazz singer. He asks her if she knows "Our Love Is Here to Stay"—naturally, she does, but at some point during the song, she looks at him, and his head is down on the keyboard, and he's shaking, she assumes, with laughter. She tells him; "Look, I know I'm no Billie Holiday, but it can't be that bad." At which point she realizes that he is sobbing—he says that "Our Love Is Here to Stay" was he and his wife Ilene's song and that she had recently committed suicide. Ilene was tragic. Unbalanced, and always threatening to kill herself, one night she said to Dad, "I'm really going to do it this time, I'm going to run out in front of the next car I see." He replied, "Sure you are—why don't you stop torturing me?" It was the last thing he'd say to her—a second later, before he knew what was happening, she bolted in front of an oncoming truck—he tried to grab her, but it was too late. She died in his arms. At the conclusion of this story, Mom and Dad embarked on their ill-advised love affair. Sheila dumped the young drummer that she was shacked up with and pregnant by, had the baby, and gave her up for adoption to a childless couple in the Bay Area. One week later, my mom and dad were married, on St. Patrick's Day (Mom's birthday), 1960, in San Francisco. They rented a small apartment in Hollywood, and fixed it up with money Mom made from the adoption. I came along in February of 1962—I'd like to think it was a happy occasion, though all the visible track marks on Mom's arms in pictures where she's holding me make me wonder. I know Dad had wanted a girl, and I looked just like him—so I guess he was pleased. My mother named me after two of the sisters in *Little Women*—Amy, the vain, feminine one, and Jo, the bookish tomboy. She later told me she'd hoped I would possess the qualities of both sisters.

Dad often talked about the night I was conceived—a particularly passionate moment in a relationship full of great passion and greater sorrow. When together, my parents seemed to bring out the worst in each other. They were both bright and tal-ented, but always competing to see who could fall the furthest and the fastest down the ladder to hell. I have a photo of myself at one and a half years old, with my very pregnant mother. When I asked her about the fate of the baby, she was dismissive and said that had definitely been some john's kid, who she ended up selling to a wealthy doctor and his wife in Bel Air. Somehow, I prevailed, sandwiched in the middle of chaos—their love child, with Dad, at least, determined to nurture me the best he could. "My little flower in the shit," he'd say. I've always felt quite privileged.

Father and daughter connecting, 1962

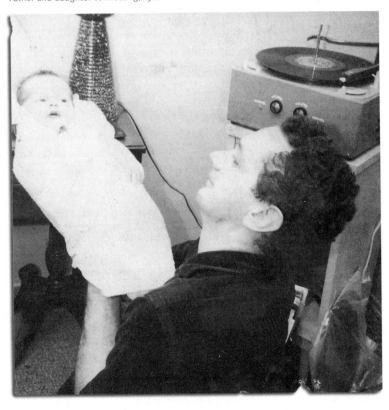

Dad told me that when I was an infant, Dizzy Gillespie dropped me on my head. It was a fact that always disturbed him greatly. He'd say, "Well, maybe he was stoned, but I think he was just trying to show off." I never understood what that meant—seems like a weird way to show off, dropping a baby. Anyway, it always bugged him—said he never trusted him after that, which I choose to take as a sign of paternal love. I often wonder if this has anything to do with the fact that I've never been a big Dizzy Gillespie fan, or if it figures into my mental problems at all—who knows.

I don't know if this is my first memory, or if I've simply heard my Dad tell this story so often that it feels like memory. In the summer of '63, I was living with my parents in Harlem. Dad was playing at the Village Gate with Charles Mingus. He would later tell me that it was "always a sweatbox" playing Mingus's music—that, coupled with his being (I think) the only ofay in the group, made for some tense situations. One day we're walking down the street, passing a newsstand, when I stop and pick up a magazine (maybe *Life*) with Thelonious Monk on the cover. I kiss it, and say, "Hi Monk." Dad, combusting with pride, picks me up, looks at me with those beautiful gray-green eyes, and says: "From now on, you're not just my baby, you're my ace-one-boon-white-coon." That, he

would claim, was the day we forever connected, and became more to each other than everything.

Sometimes, I feel I'm on the verge of remembering something. It only happens when certain elements are in place. It's always at dusk, the end of a warm day, there's a breeze, enough to flutter thin curtains, and I'm lying on my side, looking out the window. It's then that something tries to come to me, but never quite does. Mostly, it's about the air—the air has a particular quality that makes the sadness come. Then there's the sense of waiting. I'm waiting calmly for some event that I know is going to occur. Perhaps when the time is right—if ever—I'll remember. One summer afternoon, years ago when the air was similar to my memory, two men came to take away our furniture and Dad's piano. He wasn't home, but Mom was sitting on the porch in a rocking chair, too close to the edge of the stairs. One of the men asked her to move, but she wouldn't—only sat there with the faintest smile, serene as the Buddha. The man picked up the chair and dumped her out and down the stairs, as if he were emptying out a pail of water. Her head cracked open and blood flowed down the pavement, but her expression never changed. Men kept moving out furniture, just stepping over her like it was a slight imposition. "Goddamn junkies," one of

Jam session, 1957. (L-R) Joe Albany, Von Whitlock, Warne Marsh, Stan Dembowski

Dad told me that when I was an infant,
Dizzy Gillespie dropped me on my
head. It was a fact that always
disturbed him greatly.

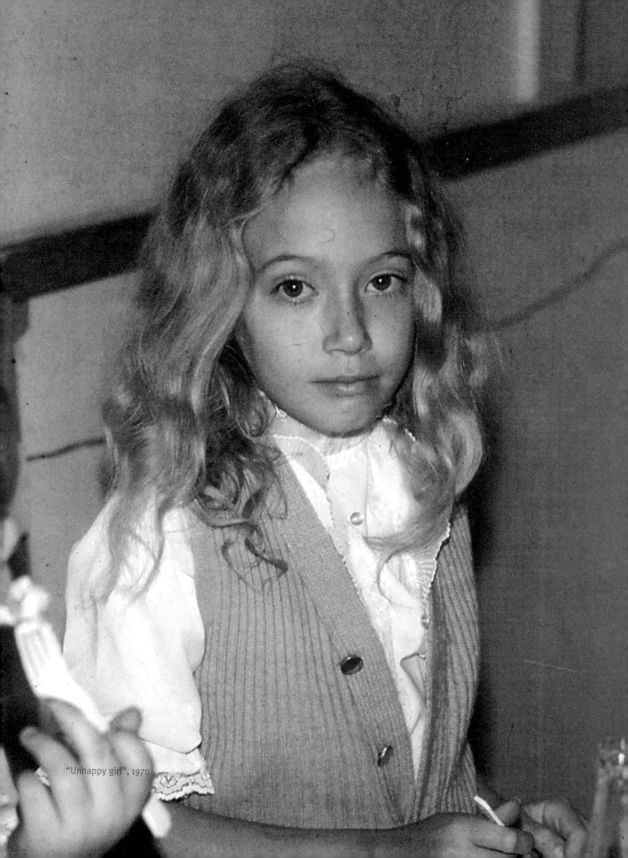

"Unhappy girl", 1970

them said. I thought she was dead, and I ran and ran, down the street to nowhere. It fades to black after that—like all my snapshot memories.

When I was about four, Dad had a regular gig at a bar in Hollywood. It was a classic dark, red-boothed, booze-drenched dive—warm and inviting. I would sit there each night with Daphne, a ravishing red-haired hooker, and Martino the bartender, aided by a number of other regulars, who would keep an eye on me while Dad played his set. I drank too many Shirley Temples, with red and green cherries, and listened to dirty jokes that I didn't get until years later. At some point, I'd be hoisted up on the piano, and I sang and danced dutifully to "Satin Doll" or "All of Me." Around eleven, I'd fall asleep and be placed behind the bar, usually on someone's fur coat, until 2 A.M., when Dad finished work. When his habit wasn't getting the best of him, he always tried his best to keep us together.

I was acutely aware, at a young age, that my life could be snuffed out in an instant. Never was this feeling stronger than when I was left in the hands of my lovely mother. Mom was petite and fair, with blue-green cat eyes—"Eyes you would happily drown in," Dad used to say. She was very hip, loved music and books, and really knew her stuff. She was

responsible for some of the best parts in *Howl*, something Ginsberg confessed to my father years after the fact. She was a mass of wasted potential. Among her talents was an uncanny ability to forge signatures. It would land her in the glass house three times. Her favorite thing to forge was medical prescriptions, and the drug she most prescribed for herself was Dilaudid. She would spend days on end semiconscious, falling off toilets, not one motherly bone in her whole beautiful body—a fact which sort of impresses me, on some twisted level. I learned early to fend for myself, foraging for food like some small freaked-out animal. When real food wasn't available, I'd invent new things to eat. Shaving cream, toothpaste, and some odd supposedly poison berries that grew on the bush outside our door. I wasn't the healthiest kid around, but I survived, which, I guess, is a good thing. I decided to make a short list in my mind of the essentials. Besides food, there was the record player for pleasure and drowning out unpleasant things, and there was sleep. To sleep, I needed pajamas, and I was very fond of my flannel PJs—I felt safe with them on. One night, when I couldn't rouse my mother out of a Dilaudid haze to dress me for bed, I ventured out into the Hollywood courtyard where we lived and started knocking on neighbors's doors for some assistance. Since it was midnight, and I was all of five years old and half naked, one would assume that a friendly face would emerge from behind a frightened door—but that was not the case. It was my first lesson in humanity. Terrified women peeked out from their curtains, shooing me away. My parents had developed a reputation as the local lunatic druggies, who played music at all hours, and I was simply their demon spawn. So there I sat, in the middle of our courtyard—it seemed huge, it was black out and freezing—a very pathetic scene. Dad was playing at a jazz club called Pepys, on Sunset Strip, and got home around 3 A.M. When he saw me waiting there, he snapped, ran into the house, and smacked Mom around. I felt some sadness for her, but not too much. At least he woke her up, and I was able to get to sleep, properly attired, and dream that I was a thousand miles away from my life. I formed a lot of opinions that night, which live with me for better or worse like tiny devils. I hate the dark and the cold and the sense of empty space around me. I have no faith in most people, particularly women, but I'm fond of coconut-lime shaving cream. I love my father. No experience is completely negative.

One Sunday, Mom takes me to the park, along with two goofballs, chased down by a bottle of Ripple. She has a way of looking perfectly elegant when she passes out—she falls with grace and picks herself up like a queen who's fallen off her throne. Halfway through the park, she is facedown in a little stream. My biggest fear is that the water spiders—or whatever the hell they are—will attack her, so I try to pull her out, but I'm a skinny kid, and it's to no avail. I decide to simply sit by her, trying to look carefree, when a man walking by stops and asks: "Is that your mom, kid, are you all right?" I assure him that all is well, and Mother is taking a short nap. My previous experiences have made me reluctant to ever ask for help again. The man leaves, but looks suspicious, and now I start really shaking her, saying the police are coming. After a seemingly endless period, she starts to shift and, after throwing up, is able to get on her feet. Somehow, we make it back to our apartment. Mom tells me affectionately: "When you were born, I could see you were Joe's baby and not some trick's kid, so I decided to keep you." One week later, she left without a word. It would be nine years before I'd see her again.

It was in late 1967 that my father worked with the great Louis Armstrong. I was an enormous fan of his from an early age and slept with a 78 of "Sugar Blues"—or maybe it was "Sugar Foot Strut"—that was pressed on blue vinyl. So it was arranged that I would accompany my dad to work one night to meet my hero. I can't remember where this club was. It was more of a hall, really, bright and big, and when we walked inside, it was wall-to-wall people. Dad, at six feet, looked over the top of the crowd, spotted Mr. Armstrong, and started pushing us through toward the front. Everyone started to part, like in a movie, and looked down at me, a sea of smiley faces that made me all the more nervous. As the last few people moved aside, there he sat, on a chair, looking straight at me, with a bigger-than-huge smile and arms outstretched. "You must be little Jo I've heard so much about," he said, drawing me to him. I corrected him that my name was Amy Jo—I was always embarrassed by my Dad's litany of nicknames. "Well, Miss Amy Jo, I've got a song that's just about you," at which time he stood me directly in front of him, while my Dad got on the piano, and I'm afraid I can't recall the other musicians—and started to sing the verse to "Once in Love with Amy." I was frozen—I kept staring at his knees. Here was this man, better than Santa or God to me, singing my song. I almost blacked out. I just kept concentrating on his kneecaps, too terrified to blink. Afterward, he gave me a hug and a sloppy kiss, and I suppose I stayed there until I fell asleep that night. Two days later, my Dad gave me an autographed picture—"To little Amy Jo, always in love with you—Pops." That became my new item to sleep with, right up to the day it mysteriously disap-

peared—probably found its way to the pawnshop. I often wish I still had that photograph, but it was mine to have for a while. Sometimes that's all you get.

In January 1968, Dad played out, and did a three-month stretch at CRC—the California Rehabilitation Center in Corona. Every couple of weeks, one of my aunts would drive my grandmother and me out there to visit him. Between the long drive and dueling perfumes that competed for space in the airtight car, I'd spend the whole trip throwing up and dry-heaving into a beige plastic bucket that was provided me for just such occasions. The prison garb at CRC was all denim, with dark blue denim button-down shirts. There was a large visiting room with round tables and slick Formica floors, great for sliding across. Dad seemed to find religion during this time, due at least in part to the fact that

In January 1968, Dad played out, and did a three-month stretch at CRC— the California Rehabilitation Center in Corona.

access to the center's piano was through the pastor. One of his strange, often beautiful letters to me began, "Darling Daughter, may the great and gentle savior smile on you, and his divine hand touch you with benevolence and benediction." It sounded like he was tripping. Visiting days were my singular source of joy, and the best parts of these visits—next to seeing Dad—were my encounters with the vending machines. There were at least ten gleaming vending machines that dispensed everything imaginable, the most impressive being a cocoa machine, which gave you the option of ordering plain, with marshmallows, or "extra rich," whatever that meant, and you could see it being made through a tiny magic win-

Each time she lunges, her patent leather purse with the gold chain strap falls down, and she keeps hitching it up, stabbing at the door. I ask my dad, "What did you do to her—why is she so mad?"

dow. While I emptied handfuls of dimes into the machines—stocking up for the pukefest on the ride home—Dad would sit with his mom and sister, listening distractedly to the latest news, hands folded on the table, head of soft curls nodding slowly, and I'd look at him and catch his eyes, and something lovely would pass between us, maybe our "connection," and I'd go home and cry to think of it, and spend much of my life looking for it in someone else.

I was now living with my grandmother. Gram was born Angela Stella Cecelia LaRocca in South Philadelphia, 1903—first generation, Sicilian and Calabrese. She was a martyred saint—the only woman I've ever loved. We lived in Hollywood at 1822 North Wilton, and I attended school when I was well enough, but usually I was sick. Sick and miserable. One consolation was the stereo—I was holding on to Dad's records. I also had a copy of Hamilton's *Greek Mythology* that I must have read twenty times. It was a comfort to read about how these gods and goddesses suffered worse than I did—Cronus eating his children, etc. Gram's cooking was the highlight during this period—nobody could cook like she did. I'd like to say more about her, but it's too painful. In the end, I repaid her kindness and sacrifice by causing her unhappiness, just like her son before me. This was a time in my life when I just did my best to dig in and make it through. I started slipping off into fantasy worlds regularly, always afraid that in one insane second, everything would collapse.

In the summer of '68, Dad and I took a Greyhound bus down to Palm Springs, where he was booked on a two-week gig with a singer named Jimmy Valentino, at some mob-run nightclub. Jimmy was sort of a Vic Damone knockoff—lots of Brylcreem and pinky rings. He smiled too often. What a mismatch they were—but times were lean, Dad took what work he could get. Once in Palm Springs, he hooked up with a local chick named Dorothy. She was very attractive, started showing up at every show, coming back to the motel at night. She seemed fairly normal, no sign of the weirdness that would come. Dad finished early at this club. Palm Springs isn't exactly hopping past a certain hour—we'd get back in time to see the last half of Johnny Carson and have a sandwich before bed. One night, Dad steps outside to refill the ice bucket when he suddenly gasps, jumps back in the room, and locks the door, telling me to get under the bed, which I don't do. Seconds later, Dorothy is pounding on the door, screaming things like "You fucking greaseball musician, I'm going to kill you!" Dad and I go to the side window and peek out to see her stabbing the door with a pair of haircutting-type scissors, and each time she lunges, her patent leather purse with the gold chain strap falls down, and she keeps hitching it up, stabbing at the door. I ask my dad, "What did you do to her—why is she so mad?" But he won't bite—just shrugs and shakes his head in disbelief. I've tried to figure it out over the years, what would've sent her off like that. Maybe he gave her the clap or something. After fifteen minutes of this, it's pretty apparent that the only thing she's going to hurt is her scissors, at which time we look at each other and start laughing until we cry—jumping on the bed, my dad doing an evil impersonation of poor old Dorothy out there. It was very surreal. The best part came two nights later, when Jimmy Valentino shows up at the club with Dorothy on his arm. Dad pulls him aside and says, "Good luck, paisan," and leaves it at that—they didn't get along too well. Other than the nutty-dame incident, the only other highlight in the desert was meeting Frank Sinatra. He came into the club one night, listened to the music for a couple of hours, and waved my Dad over during his twenty-minute break. They had an animated chat about New Jersey, their mothers, baseball, just a couple of nice Italian boys. He bought me a Shirley Temple, shook my dad's hand, told him, "You've got a great book, kid," put a hundred dollars in the tip kitty, and left. A fairly boring story, but if you meet someone like Sinatra, I guess it's worth a mention. I've been down to Palm Springs a few times since then without my dad, but didn't care for it too much. Anywhere I went with him sparkled like a fun fair. He was my very favorite person.

Dad and I lived at the St. Francis Hotel on Hollywood Boulevard, just west of Western. There was a fire escape outside our window. Fire escapes are sublime. I spent endless days and nights out there, watching madness and nothing at all from the safety of three stories up. The old Hollywood House of Billiards was catty-corner to the hotel. I loved seeing the sharp-looking hustlers with alligator cue cases and the not-so-sharp suckers, who'd get drunk and grifted, come and go. L.A.'s a strange place. Overall, it's just a big, lazy beach town, but there are pockets, like the corner of Hollywood and Western, that are always alive. If the fire escape was my sanctuary, then staying in the care of Koko the clown was my damnation. Dad wasn't working too much around this time, and his habit was raging. However, his reputation did land him the occasional job. Some of his gigs were in hard-core titty bars, a fact that was both sad and demeaning for a musician of his caliber. It was during these seedy jobs that I would be left with our friendly neighbor Koko, who—according to him—was Barnum and Bailey's biggest star back in

his day. He was like the sideshow geek in Nightmare Alley, very freaky, did a lot of mescaline if I remember right. He made me a very nervous six-year-old. He had lots of little games he liked to play, like find Mr. Elephant—a can-you-grab-the-elephant's-trunk (a.k.a. his dick) kind of game. He never could get me to do it. I was a fairly sharp kid, and just sat in silent repulsion while he squealed and jumped around, basically got himself off. To his credit, he never hurt me, never forced me into anything. I think he adored me, in his own way. He would always bring me little broken toys he'd found, and make up songs—"A. J. is an angel bright who lights up Koko clownie's night." I never told my father—I knew he would kill him if he found out, and then I'd really be screwed. A year later, Koko threw himself over a freeway overpass and died. Dad was hesitant to tell me. "Koko has gone away A. J., but he liked you very much." Indeed he did.

There was one other kid at the St. Francis, named LaPrez Johnson. He was a nine-year-old mulatto who had a glorious auburn Afro and wild green eyes. I was now seven, very pale and suspicious. Being ingenious street kids, we made up games using what few resources were available to us. Our favorite game was called Jump the Bum. Simply put, you jumped over a street bum until he (ladies were off limits) got pissed off enough to make a grab for you, or, if he really had some moxie, got up and chased you away. On a bad day, you'd get "dead bums"—too tired or loaded to budge no matter how much you provoked them. One time, LaPrez was mid-leap over our latest victim when out of nowhere, the bum pulls out a broken bottle and slashes open LaPrez's ankle. It took twenty stitches, and kept him out of commission for the rest of the summer. On reflection, perhaps it was a cruel game, but most of the bums were good sports—almost looked forward to the attention. It isn't like any of us had anything better to do. LaPrez lived with his mother, a very pretty but badly strung-out hooker. Under the circumstances, I always thought he was a well-adjusted kid, always able to laugh, much more than me—I was eternally sullen. One night La Prez came to our room and asked my dad if he could give him some help with his mother. When he opened the door to their room, she was sitting straight up on her Murphy bed, eyes wide and staring at us, scarf still tied around her arm. She was blue, dead at least an hour. In the hotel lobby, there was a TV set that three of the resident rummies had total control over, twenty-four hours a day; usually horse races or cop shows were on, but for this one fucked-up night, they sat us down on their smelly old-man sofa and let us watch cartoons. LaPrez stared, serious and silent,

"High times" at Grant Elementary School. 1970

at the television, and I stared at him. He was staring at Top Cat when the coroners wheeled out his mother, and he did not look up when the police came, inquiring about next of kin. (None.) Nor did he move when my dad, crying, handed them a bag of LaPrez's belongings. Then, the cops walked over to him and said something ridiculous like "Come with us, son." It was then that he turned and looked at me, expectant and drowning, and I did nothing. I could have taken his hand or, even better, told him to run. Maybe we both should have run, but my father was sick and needed me—I could never desert him. After that, I was the only kid at the St. Francis. I was like Eloise without the frills and sweet attention. Sometimes it was hell, yet it was our home, and it was fine.

Dad at twenty, Los Angeles, 1944

There was the Big Owl drugstore to the southeast corner, where I'd shoplift, and Broadway on the southwest, where I'd do likewise.

I always looked forward to our weekly visit to the musicians' union on Vine Street. Dad would go in to check for possible work and take a minute to flirt with Agnes at the front desk, who hounded him because his dues were in arrears. They had a recreation room there, with a pool table and television, where I'd go to watch the guys shoot eight ball, though with all the smoke, it was pretty hard to see. After these visits, we'd head north, to the late great corner of Hollywood and Vine. I thought it was tops, even as late as '68, '69. There was the Big Owl drugstore to the southeast corner, where I'd shoplift, and Broadway on the southwest, where I'd do likewise. There was the Firefly, where my dad and Charlie Parker had played— though perhaps not together—and the Brown Derby with the fancy bamboo room next door, where I went once for my birthday. Best of all was the Entrée Cafeteria, the best ever cafeteria in my opinion. Every time we walked in, Billy Barty would be holding court at one of the tables, and somehow, my dad knew him. He would wave us over, always with a cigar in his mouth, and have me sit in his lap. It was a little strange, sitting in a midget's lap, but I adored him. He was hyper-animated, as were his circle of colorful friends—guys with names like Lefty, an ex-middleweight southpaw, and Jocko, the alcoholic jockey. I would sit eating my neon Jell-O, in sheer heaven, listening to their stories. It was better than Damon Runyon. My dad, being very funny, a big boxing fan and an old movie buff, fit in nicely with everyone. Billy called him "Jersey Joe." All of these places are gone now, but back then, the four corners of Hollywood and Vine held some of my brightest memories.

Dad had a couple of friends living at the Knickerbocker Hotel over on Ivar, the most interesting being a guy named Izzy, who made a living doing astrological charts. Izzy informed my dad that on the fourth, fifth, and sixth of February in 1962, a mass of people in India ran to the top of a mountain because the planets were all aligned, which signaled either the end of the world or the birth of the new messiah. Since I was born February 5, 1962, Izzy fixed on the idea that my life should be closely monitored, and insisted that we visit him on a regular basis so he could see what was new in my chart. He had a studio apartment on the eighth floor that looked south to Hollywood Boulevard, and four cats that stank up the place—plus he never cracked a window and chain-smoked cigars. Izzy would answer the door in a red Chinese robe. He had the countenance of a kindly bookie—always played jazz, knew my dad from Greenwich Village back in '44 where he'd been a local scenester, respected writer, great music supporter. However, times change, and those who

don't change get steamrolled into oblivion—that's what happened to Izzy, who'd been living at the Knickerbocker for fourteen years, since '55. He'd decided to hole himself up, surrounded by his memories and passions. Hotels in Hollywood and downtown L.A. are full of forgotten people like that. People you wouldn't look twice at, with their hot plates and old slippers, but you should look, because they're far more interesting than all the rich assholes swanning around Beverly Hills, full of themselves and nothing else. The last time I saw Izzy was late '72. I was with my grandmother at the beauty salon inside the Knickerbocker, and I see him, there in the lobby, having his shoes shined. "Hey Starshine, what's new? Done anything astounding yet?" He always called me Starshine, owing, I guess, to my rare astrological pedigree. "Not yet—how you, Izzy?" "Ah, hanging on the ropes, kid—so your dad is abroad and doing well?" "Yes, I'm glad he wrote to you," I said. "He hasn't written me—I saw it in the stars." And I've always believed that he did.

We had some strange neighbors in Hollywood. A few were old spinsters who felt compelled to offer me guidance, whether I wanted it or not. One such lady was Mrs. Culver ("of the Culver City Culvers") who decided that the only hope for me and my delinquency was to accept Jesus into my heart. She asked my father if she could take me to her Protestant church on Sunday, but he was wary—"Well, we're Catholics, I wouldn't want to confuse her." However, she persisted and in the end prevailed. Bright and early Sunday, to church we went, accompanied by her greasy, creepy nephew, Ernest, who was the kind of guy that was always jerking off in the bushes when I walked to school. First impression, upon arrival, is that it's quite an ugly church, and all of the people in it are dressed badly. Mrs. Culver hightails it over to the preacher, and talks to him frantically, gesturing at me, who he glances at gravely a few times. Then begin the endless hokey hymns and droning sermons. At some point, I realize this alienlike preacher has honed in on me—which I'm slow to notice since I'm mentally light-years away by now. I hear him say, "Friends, look upon this poor child who is not in God's flock"—something like that—then Mrs. Culver and Ernest take me by the elbows and start walking me down the aisle toward this weirdo, who is getting louder and holding out his arms to me while the congregation stares, and some cry, at which point I decide I won't be sacrificed without a fight, and start screaming, trying to make a break for it, as the alien yells, "Satan is taking hold of the girl," and I think, "Pal, if Satan were to show up now, I'd go flying happily into his red-hot arms

to escape this God-fearing freak show." After much hullaballoo, my torment ended, and I left the preacher with double shin scrapes down both legs to remember me by. When I got home, my dad took one look at me, now in hysterical overdrive, and said: "Oh, little Jo—I am so sorry." Mrs. Culver was standing back a little in the hallway looking sheepish. Dad said: "Keep away from my daughter, you fucking witch," and slammed the door as she was telling him she would pray for us both. From that moment on, I detested all organized religions, though I enjoyed reading about the lives of the saints, like Saint Agatha, who was sodomized and had her nipples torn off after refusing to let herself be deflowered by the local menfolk—such dedication to any belief truly inspired me. I'd play a game called Saints where I'd test my pain threshold, poking myself with sharp objects, sticking my fingers in the fire, trying to make my palms bleed, etc. I concluded that Christians (WASPs in particular) were generally unimaginative creeps, and I've seen little over the years to convince me otherwise.

Dad signed up for the methadone program in January of 1970, and we moved into a little studio apartment on Gramercy Place. Just when things seemed to be looking up, Dad got busted on Valentine's Day for some probation violation. Early on the evening of the fourteenth, I was waiting for him to return from the store. We were planning a Valentine's party, I guess for two broken-down sweethearts. I was listening to Fats Waller's "Fat and Greasy," which was some of my feeling-good music, as opposed to Billie singing "What's New?" which I'd play when I was low. Anyway, I was looking out the window for Dad when I spotted a cop car and an unmarked vehicle with two poorly disguised pigs inside. The uniforms would look up at the window occasionally, but the narcs stared straight ahead. Half an hour they sat, but in our neighborhood stakeouts were a common sight, so I didn't give it much thought. Then up the drive sauntered my father. I wish I could describe his walk—it was most musical and swinging, like all his gestures. He was carrying a bag and looked up at the window, started to wave, then spotted the cops, and they spotted him. They jumped out, grabbed his hand that was still in mid-wave, pulled it down between his legs, pulled his other hand up between his legs, and cuffed him that way—like a contortionist. They were pushing him into the back of the unmarked car, just as I got outside. He was looking at me yelling, "Everything's okay"—very unconvincing. I look at the ground at all the things that spilled out of his bag. Little candy hearts with sayings like "GROOVY," "KISS ME," etc., hot dogs, a couple of Yahoos, and a card. The

illustration on the card was classic liquor-store art, with a cartoon guy who looked like Mr. Magoo, with a big red nose, striped prison garb, and a ball and chain with hearts around it. It said, "I'm just a prisoner of your love." I reached down for it, but an officer grabbed me from behind—his mistake. I scratched, spit, and punched trying to get my hands on that card, to no avail. Things got pretty vague after that. I think I had a major asthma attack, as I was inclined to do when under duress. At that point in my life, I had seen a few fairly nasty things—but to this day, the thought of that card can cause me more pain and make me cry more deeply than all the loss and sorrow in the world. After Dad went down, they decreased his methadone dose from

I decide I won't be sacrificed without a fight, and start screaming, trying to make a break for it, as the alien yells, "Satan is taking hold of the girl."

ninety to ten milligrams a day as "punishment." Of course all that did, besides making him sick as hell, was force him to supplement—and so he was off again.

Terry loved Dad. She cooked for him, occasionally copped for him, and was a big jazz fan. When he was abusive, she cried silent, dignified tears. Her appearance was striking. Waist-length honey hair, neatly pressed minis, matching bags and shoes. Terry was a transvestite, born Terence E. Pruitt. She would say (I must say "she," never having seen her as "he") that if real women spent half the time she did "enhancing their femininity," the world would be full of happy men. She

After being picked up on a second charge of pandering and possession, Terry cut a deal with the DA to avoid a two-year stretch in a men's prison—her worst fear.

was forever saving money for her sex-change operation, and Dad was forever blowing her savings on smack. To further complicate her life, she got saddled with the responsibility of caring for me. She proved herself a much better mother than my natural one. She baked cookies, put me in French braids with blue ribbons (to match my eyes) and even joined the PTA—June Cleaver with a dick. Unfortunately, some concerned father had figured out that she was a he, and made the mistake of confronting her after school one day. Now, Terry Femme, in her prior incarnation, had been known as "Terror" Pruitt, Junior Golden Gloves—and with one left jab to the sternum, set this asshole on his knees, winded. She smoothed out her skirt, gently took my hand, and earned herself a place on my short list of heroines. However, this scene of twisted domesticity was short-lived. Terry had never had a real habit—just the occasional "joy bang," as they say—but soon she was using in earnest. She was so tormented, one couldn't blame her. Maybe she was testing Dad's devotion, seeing if he'd intervene, she pined over him so. The problem is, junkies are usually self-absorbed, and I don't think he noticed her decline—but I did. She started turning tricks and, after being picked up on a second charge of pandering and possession, cut a deal with the DA to avoid a two-year stretch in a men's prison—her worst fear. After informing on her dealer, she simply disappeared, and I never saw her again. So began one of life's little slumps. School became simply unbearable. Even in Hollywood, my home life was fodder for gossip. Now I had my father picking me up, stoned, at the front of the school. One boy took to impersonating his strung-out state for the class's amusement—a teacher included, who seemed to get the biggest bang out of it. This went on for a few days until I finally snapped. It was Thursday when I kicked the offensive boy's (Dougie's) ass. I bloodied his nose and cut his lip, and when they finally pulled me off of him, I had a black clump of his hair clutched in my hand. Since I was on a roll, I called my teacher Mrs. Ballie an ugly old cunt and, at eight years old was expelled from Grant Elementary School.

My musical education at the hands of my dad was both exhilarating and, at times, a terrible drag. Dad expected so much from me, which I'm not knocking, but I was a fairly average eight-year-old, capable of retaining only so much information. Since I was his daughter, and tuned into him on other levels, he assumed that I had the same ability that he did to understand jazz. Of course, I had only been listening to music for a quarter of the time he'd been playing it. I was barraged with technical terms and abstract theories. He was very keen on contemporary composers like Schoenberg too—but the whole atonal thing made me weep with confusion, so he laid off of that, and we stuck with jazz. As much as I love jazz, when forced to analyze and recognize every flattened fifth, suspended harmony, and mop-mop lick, it would start to grind me down. I was a nervous wreck when we listened to music together, because I knew I'd fail the test to come—usually figuring out the origins of bebop tunes, what popular songs they were derived from. I sucked at that, much to my dad's dismay. "You mean you can't hear that 'Hot House' is 'What Is This Thing Called Love?' What a tin ear." Oh well, I fared better with the standards, knew most of them after the first couple notes of the verse, but that was memorization, plain and simple. One Father's Day, I bought Dad some Bird anthology, and told him that I liked the track "My Old Flame." He let me know that this particular recording was a very poor one. "He's so loaded—can't you hear all the spit in his reed?" Guess not. Anyway, I'm very grateful for those learning sessions, and I'd like to think that if he were still around, he might be half pleased with my efforts to keep learning, and very pleased that the love of music he instilled in me has helped me pull through some rough times.

One of Dad's best friends was Dalton, a fascinating guy who made porno

My "Ace-one-boon-white-coon," 1982

movies for a living. From what I gathered, he was quite a talented filmmaker. They had met years earlier at an after-hours club on the strip, where fellow hipsters like Lenny Bruce, Terry Southern, Joe Mani, and others would get together after 2 A.M. to talk, goof off, mostly listen to music. In the spring of '71, Dad was in trouble with the law again. To hear him tell it, he had tried to cop, Mickey Mouse showed, he got twisted and violated. In English: he was buying dope, the cops showed, and he was sentenced for the buy and violating his parole. Most of the grownups around me spoke in a sort of code. Instead of standing sentence, we hid out at Dalton's, and I soon learned the language of blue movies. Any innocence I had left would soon be gone. Dalton's house was in North Hollywood, and he had a son a couple of years older than me named Monty. There was a large detached backhouse where some films were shot. During our stay, Dalton was working on a series of "sexual enlightenment" films— "real bon-a-roo sex education," he'd say. Monty and I were always spying through the windows at the weird and wondrous sights. I saw an Indian guru performing auto-fellatio and auto-anal sex. There were demonstrations concerning the attainment of various orgasms. Fusion, Tantric, Altered States—after the initial shock wore off, all the writhing, moaning nakedness seemed commonplace. The house was filled with books and "sexual research" papers. Being an avid reader, I was kept busy reading everything I could get my hands on. Monty and I made up a dirty word game, the object being to see who could come up with the most genital slang words like snapper, cooze, lizard, short arm, quim, rod, snatch, box—I can't remember them all now, but I usually triumphed. Dad during this time was quite happy. He had a piano to play, plenty of hash and other fun things, and women galore. Dalton was always hooking him up. He'd say, "Ladies, you are in the pres-

ence of greatness. This is the Legendary Joe Albany." Chicks really dug my dad. I guess it had to do with this very sweet, almost old-fashioned quality he possessed. I remember walking in on him and Dalton with two skin-flick starlets while he was reciting the poem: "I think that I shall never see a poem as lovely as a tree," etc. The girls were all giggles and coos, and Dalton, stoned as usual, was saying, "That's beautiful, man." There was a big buzz going around, about some little blue pills that everyone referred to as "jolly beans." They seemed to make whoever was taking them terribly happy, and since I liked the name, I snaked one out of its hiding place and tried it. What a blast—that was the day I fell in love with speed. There was other stuff—Mazola parties—your typical swinging L.A. jazz/porn scene. It was great there, and I was sad when we had to leave. It seemed to be our destiny to keep on the move, like a couple of unhappy sharks.

We spent a lot of time walking to Fern Dell, a park in the middle of Hollywood, right off Western and Los Feliz. Fern Dell was a haven for social outcasts—hippies, musicians, homeless folk. Sometimes we'd be accompanied by a couple of Dad's friends—Bob Whitlock, Art Pepper, or Lester Hobbs (a trumpet player who had two fingers missing from his right hand, the result of shooting up between his fingers, having exhausted all his veins). It was interesting to see the way these original hip cats adapted to the style of the times. They all had sideburns, longer hair, paisley shirts with big lapels, flairs—but they still shined their shoes. All in their late forties at the time, they were still the kings of cool.

One Sunday, we headed to Fern Dell with Art, Lester, and two friends of mine, Gerald and Lorna, the black albino siblings. They looked pretty strange, with their big white afros and pink eyes like white rabbits. The other kids at my new school were terrified of them, due in great part to the fact that the movie The Omega Man had recently come out, and everyone thought they were atomic zombies—they cleared the hallways. The Omega Man was playing at the Star Theatre with Billy Jack—a kid's dream double bill in 1971. I, being the official friend of the friendless, hooked up with Gerald and Lorna when the three of us got socked away together in corrective—or "retarded" as the other kids called it—P.E. I was there because of my asthma, and they were in with light- and-heat sensitivity problems. There we were at Fern Dell, three jazz junkies, two black albinos and myself, along with loads of flower children, recorders, dogs, and naked babies. Dad had just bought me a portable six-inch Sony TV that came with a battery pack that was larger than the television

itself. We decided to take it to the park for a test run. The Brain That Wouldn't Die was on Chiller, which was my favorite show. This TV must have been one of the first portables, judging from the excitement it generated. We ended up with a dozen people crowded around this six-inch screen, smoking pot and watching Chiller. Dad, Lester, and Art were having wasted laughing fits, making dumb jokes about getting head from the severed head of the woman in the movie. This was on the same day that my dad met some hippie chick named Melodie, who lived in a commune over on Van Ness. Very pretty and very strange. She ate cat food and had a son my age who'd shit in old tires in their backyard. One week after this Chiller-in-the-park lovefest, Dad hocked my beloved TV set. I remember feeling angry with him for the first time. It was then I realized that no love, however deep, remains unspoiled forever.

By the end of '71, my dad was boxed into a bad corner. All over town, cops, pushers, and psychos were after him with various axes to grind. Around Christmas of '71, Dad was contacted by an English music promoter who said he could keep him working in Europe, book him into all the jazz festivals. Since work seemed to have dried up in L.A., shitty town for jazz that it is, Dad took him up on the offer and left for England. Over the next eight years, I would join him for brief periods. We lived in Denmark for a while and got to see a lot of Dexter Gordon, who I adored, but never again would it just be us two, each surviving for the sake of the other. After he left, I lived with my grandmother. The general consensus was that it would be good for me to settle down into a normal life, but a normal life held little appeal for me. On the day I went to the airport to see him off, he was upbeat and said he'd send for me as soon as possible. We said goodbye, and I was watching him walk toward the plane when he spun around and yelled "Ace-one-boon-white-coon, you're the nuttiest!"—and then he was gone, and I felt my spirit drop out the bottom of my shoes, rarely seen again. The only joyful thing that I did around this time was start collecting records. I bought the *Velvet Underground* and the *Clockwork Orange* soundtrack, and I stole *Led Zeppelin III* and the Stone's *Their Satanic Majesties Request*, figuring the latter two bands didn't need my money as much—ever a thief with a conscience. Dad left me his jazz LPs, so now I forged out on my own, musically. While he was in Europe, his career took off. He released a lot of LPs. It made me feel that I had somehow kept him down when he was with me. Not quite a jinx, but certainly no good-luck charm. On the other hand, I felt I had been deserted. I had often sacrificed my childhood to play parent, but maybe he had sacrificed his art to play parent to me. I became a mass of pissed-off rebellion. Boys, petty crime, drugs—the usual suspects.

In 1972, a correspondence began between my grandmother and my mother's sister, who lived in San Francisco. It was arranged that I would travel up north for visits four times a year, to acquaint myself with the other side of the family and perhaps fill some of the hole left by my father's departure. Around this time, I was hit hard by the onslaught of early puberty. I began menstruating at ten, had an obscene C-cup chest at eleven, and at the age of twelve, during one of my Frisco visits, was seduced by my mother's kid brother, Uncle John, who was twenty-one years old. There were those who knew and did nothing. Tragic, all the dirty little secrets we allow to live comfortably on our backs. These sexual episodes continued until I was fifteen, at which time, with the help of lots of amphetamines, I found sufficient confidence to tell him I wanted it to end. After I said my piece, he looked at me with anger, perhaps some fear, then jumped on his motorcycle and drove wildly away, without a word. That evening, a call came at my aunt's house. John had lost control of his bike and crashed into a concrete retaining wall, dying on impact, his neck broken. I wasn't sure how I should feel. For a moment,

I felt I was to blame, but that passed quickly. There were others who felt that that was the case, and let me know it by their expressions of extreme distaste, or by the way they'd refuse to look at me at all, but I was never one to back the popular opinion. Soon after my uncle's death, I decided that the time had come to look up my mother. It had been nine years since I'd last seen her, and I knew she was living in some Tenderloin hotel. After my aunt reluctantly divulged her address, I headed over, full of nervous anticipation, only to find she wasn't home, although her door was open. I walked in and saw two finches chirping blithely in a small cage on the window ledge. There was an empty pack of cigarettes and a beat-up paperback of the poems of e. e. cummings, with a recent picture of myself tucked in like a bookmark. I hoped this was a good sign. In the lobby I asked where I might find Sheila Regis, as she was now known, and was told to check the bar around the corner. Out on the street, just as I turned off Fifth onto Market, I saw a small heap slumped on the pavement. Something made me stop, for I had seen this configuration before. I went down on one knee and peered beneath the black bobble cap that was pulled down low over a tangle of gray-red hair, at what remained of my mother's once-fair face. "Can I help you, Mom?" Her eyes opened slowly and turned to me. "You look like a slut," she said, with a vague smile, then simply closed her eyes and said no more. I kept kneeling, with one hand on her shoulder, taking in what she had said. I was wearing a pale pink shirtdress, flat ballet slippers I always favored, no makeup, hair tied back. Had she looked into my soul? Did she know about the relationship I'd had with her brother—did she blame me like the rest of them? Oh Father, Father, where were you? I stood up and took three large steps backward—then jumped over her tiny broken body with one deft leap. Fuck 'em all. I closed my eyes and never looked back. I headed over to the Mission, where I knew I could score some heroin from a guy I'd met while browsing in a record store. That night and for many nights to come, I would dive into the bottomless darkness of my life and sink all the way down. It was a beautiful drowning.

"Can I help you, Mom?" Her eyes opened slowly and turned to me. "You look like a slut," she said, with a vague smile, then simply closed her eyes and said no more.

Two Poems

by

Thomas Sayers Ellis

Undressing Mr. Wiggles
FOR OVERTON LLOYD

A semi-bionic
irreducible commodity,
both hit and splash
and metafoolish
as red panties and fins
on letterforms—all drawn
under the influence
of seaweed, reason
for the tank harmonics,
bubbly vocalizations
and liquid licks.
All graffilthy.

Your funkentelechy
gave birth to the nation.

Overseer of wiggling blackness,
first line dance and final splank.

Antitour all antiwar.

Off the hook, hooked and a hook.

Not hung or hung up

on earholes, clothes, clones,

or his own bones

like some kissed egos

we know. Pure woo.

Throbassonic wetness and perfection.

Life force and downstroke.

Deep togetherness.

The potential existence

of a nation is to rise.

All-night crazoid craving for liquid sunshine.

Finger-in-their-hole

and non-profish from day-one.

Boptist and blowpole.

Only yo-yo and wheels

not in fatigues and sync.

Go wiggle or go skate.

Only bait no feet to fail him.

Just the skin and swim he's in

and the swim and skin
skins hit him in.
A Vaseline victory.

A man with no imagination
has no wet dream.

Black Freekdom: Suzie Thundertussy, Octavepussy
and the Motor-Booty Girls,
Giggles and Squirm.
Something stank and the yellow bird
above concert ate some.
Ring-around-the-record-companies.
Small musty halls
instead of large, sold-out ones.
Butt-to-butt resuscitation.
The magic rhythm
by which all defunkatized juices
become revitalized.
Butterflyworms.

Album cover your ears
and come in and throw down.

Groovallegiance

FOR MICHAEL VEAL

A dream. A democracy. A savage liberty.

And yet another anthem and yet another heaven

and yet another party wants you.

Wants you wants you wants you.

Wants you to funk-a-pen funkapuss.

Wants you to anthologize then retroop your group.

Wants you to recruit prune juice.

My peeps.

My poetics.

My feet.

All one.

All one.

All one, heel and toe.

My peeps.

My poetics.

My feet.

All one.

All one.

All one, lowly heel and toe.

Br'er feet and br'er beat repeatedly beaten.

Repeatedly beaten repeatedly beaten.

Br'er feet and br'er beat repeatedly beaten.

Repeatedly beaten repeatedly beaten repeatedly beaten.

Br'er feet and br'er beat repeatedly beaten.

Feet feet feet.

Every feet a foot and free, every feet a foot and free,
every feet a foot and free.

A foot and free.

Agony and defeat, a foot and free.

A foot and free.

Every feet a foot and free, every feet a foot and free,
every feet a foot and free.

A foot and free.

Agony and defeat, a foot and free.

A foot and free.

Reverend feet, a foot and free. Reverend feet,
repeatedly beaten.

Feet feet feet.

A million marchers.

Two parties.

One Washington.

One Washington.

Two parties.

A million marchers.

An afterparty.

An afterparty after marching.

The aftermarch.

An aftermarch-afterparty after marching
all the way to Washington.

Another march another party.

Another aftermarch after another afterparty.

After another afterparty after marching.

After another march afterpartying and after marching
all the way to Washington.

Always Washington always Washington.

Uncle Jam, enjambed
all the way to Washington.

After all that marching after all that partying.

Uncle Jam, enjambed.

Always Washington.

A million marchers.

Two parties.

One Washington.

One Washington.

Two parties.

A million marchers.

Footwork.

If feet work for page shouldn't feet work
for stage, run-on.

Run-on platform.

Run-on floor,
run-on.

If feet work abroad shouldn't feet work
at home, run-on.

Run blood, run-off.

From run flag.

From run bag,
run-on.

Run and tell it.

Run tell tag run tell toe, run tell, tell it.

De-decorate intelligence.

If so also de-decorate form. If so also de-decorate war,
run home.

In every war bloods leave and bloods bleed
and don't come home. What for in every war,
what for, and don't come home.

For war for war for war.

In every war bloods leave and bloods bleed
and don't come home. What for in every war,
what for, and don't come home.

For more for more for more.

That for, in every war.

That for, for every drug.

The war on drugs is a war on bloods,
run tell it.

A line is played. A section plays.

All up, into it, and involved, into it into it
and involved, all up into it and involved.

Footnote.

Take joke.

Take note to toes.

Clip note.

Go home.

Take note to foot.

Race note.

Footnote to feet.

Foot hurt.

Footnote to note.

Cite hurt.

Toe note to foot.

Bottoms up.

Sorefoot to church.

Stop running.

If office if oath.

Broken votes.

A line is played. A section plays.

A protest you press to test repeating itself.

A section plays. A line is played.

A protest you press to test repeating itself.

My peeps.

My poetics.

My feet.

Some ally.

Some enemy.

Mostly tradition.

The jive end.

Br'er rear.

Br'er rear end isms.

Pass out the words.

The kitty is not a toy.

I owe roots and books to groundwork's underground crosstalk of African Telephone Churches.

All one all one all one, star-spangled funky.

BY RICK MOODY

Dolmen Music
blew into his
life like a voice
from beyond
and stayed

on MEREDITH MONK

In college I was in love with a dancer. It was *a mess*, as college romances often are. It was a mess even after college, flaring up in conflagrations that probably left both of us sad. Couldn't stay together exactly, nor could we part. Now she's a social worker and psychologist with kids and a lawyer husband. A friend recently ran into her, in that Upper West Side citadel of kitchen gizmos, Zabar's. I don't know what she was buying. Her account would differ from mine, obviously.

Back in college she was a dancer and she was spectacularly beautiful and I was in love with her. She was tiny and thin. She'd had the inevitable tangle with anorexia. She never finished reading books. There was always a stack of half-finished books on her night table. She liked Roland Barthes and Michel Foucault, and I think she was for a while the subtenant of Sylvere Lotringer, editor of *Semiotexte*. These things didn't help her finish any book that I ever saw.

Whereas I had known nothing about dance in high school beyond the occasional auditorium presentation of ballet at which my attendance was compulsory and at which I was mostly bored, I now learned a lot about dance. My problem with dance, prior to this crash course, had to do with *tote bags*. I didn't want to end up one of those people with a *tote bag* that I was lugging around to cultural events, expatiating on how great the ballet was.

It's the condition of youth eternally to imagine that your time, your era, is a time of unprecedented ferment. All is possibility, and the intellectual ideas to which you are being exposed suggest infinite permutations, all of them impressive. I'm sure it was true for Lee, and it was true for me. I remember (heatedly) suggesting to her, one night, that she had to make a dance where the only accompaniment was the *amplified sound of the dancers breathing*. She said it had been done. Instead, Lee choreographed a piece for dancers with tennis rackets. I don't think she had played the game since her unrewarding

teen lessons at the country club in Mamaroneck. Yet somehow she made the tennis racket, in the context of a dance studio, look like a Greco-Roman shield.

Another choreographer of our acquaintance, David, was at the same time making a piece for nondancers, in which I performed myself. This was noteworthy because I had almost no natural grace, and I was unable to commit movement combinations to memory. Lee once attempted to teach me a phrase from a master class she'd been to: I couldn't even raise one arm and jump simultaneously. Luckily, the piece David was making consisted *entirely* of Sufi spins, a movement strategy favored by contemporary choreographers for its elegance and grace. To put it bluntly, all I had to do onstage was spin around and around and around and try to avoid falling over. There were a number of things you could do in order to avoid falling over while doing Sufi spins. After all, the Sufis had been performing them for centuries.

The text of our piece was from Gertrude Stein, "As a Wife Loves a Cow: A Love Story." It was an opaque but hilarious Stein composition, which was musical and fanciful in equal measure: *Nearly all of it to be as a wife has a cow, a love story. All of it to be as a wife has a cow, all of it to be as a wife has a cow, a love story.* And so forth. There was some unison recitation at the beginning of the dance and then each of us (Lee, David, myself, a guy called Ed) recited a paragraph, and then there was again some unison at the end. It was almost impossible to memorize Stein, I found, because it didn't *mean anything* in the usual way. I had memorized a lot of dramatic writing in college, I'd acted in various plays, and, if you had a sense of where you were going, you could, in the course of things, memorize the words. In Stein, you had *no idea* where you were going, so remembering the prose was a matter of counting repetitions, *We feel we feel. We feel or if we feel if we feel or if we feel. We feel or if we feel. As it is made made a day made a day or two made a day, as it is made a day or two, as it is made a day. Made a day. Made a day.* Even typing it is hard. The good news was if you got lost in the Stein text, you could just repeat what you were saying for a while. No one would notice.

Actually being able to dance, even in this very primitive, ritualistic way, is one of the happy memories of college for me. But just as galvanizing as the experience of trying to do Sufi spins while reciting Stein was rehearsing. David always encouraged us to *improvise* in order to get

warmed up, and there were certain records that were really good for *improvising* in the dimly lit dance studio, with its fabulous sound system, and these albums are themselves records of this particular time of ferment: *Music for Eighteen Musicians* by Steve Reich and Musicians, *Einstein on the Beach*, by Philip Glass, *The Name of This Band Is Talking Heads*, by Talking Heads, *My Life in the Bush of Ghosts*, by David Byrne and Brian Eno, and *Dolmen Music*, by Meredith Monk.

Lee had given me *Dolmen Music* for Christmas. I remember some disclaimer: *Seems like it might be something you'd like.* So the record was part of our conversation, part of our *hocket*, which is a form that Monk herself has used, a duet in which the two singers finish parts of each other's musical lines, as in Monk's duet with the singer and musician Robert Een, where the two voices are so carefully listening to one another that you aren't always sure who's singing what, nor who is finishing for whom. In baroque music it was considered *very funny*, the hocket. It was part of the human comedy.

Dolmen Music blew through my life like an intercessory voice from the beyond. To say I had never heard anything like it was probably not entirely true, because there are a few things that were not *absolutely* unlike it, some of Yoko Ono, maybe a few jazz singers, like Fitzgerald, maybe some of early Joni

Mitchell. But these examples represent just a small piece of the technical strategy in Meredith Monk's music, and they don't get, at all, to the *mood* of her pieces, which always comes first. In fact, even *mood* is the wrong word, because it would be like saying that *black rage* is a mood, or *unrestrained grief* is a mood, or *the ecstasy of the spirit* is a mood. Often, in Monk's music, several of these moods coexist or overlap. As in the case of *Dolmen Music*, which begins with a piece called "Gotham Lullaby." The *song*, since it is just soloist and piano, begins with an iteration of the chords, the accompaniment on piano, after which Monk joins, in one of her unrestrained lyrical modes, singing something like a conventional statement of the melody, but without words, or rather with words in some tongue otherwise unknown, twice through thus, and then she launches herself up into the high end of her soprano, doing some staccato quarter tones over the piano part (which never changes), then back to the melody as stated at the outset. Something ghostly hovers over the piano in the distance—a faint violin part? The piano plays through its cycle of chords one more time, and the lullaby is over. At the end of the piece, you can hear Monk's foot slip off the sustain pedal. It's a spectral, affecting performance. Somehow the song completely breaks through whatever impenetrabilities you have erected around yourself. In its wordlessness, maybe. Which is probably why Monk almost never sets texts. Or maybe it has to do with the microtonality of the middle of the song, with the way she flirts with and resists the tonal home of the key in which the piece is composed. Or maybe it has to do with the folk-music repetitions and simplicity of "Gotham Lullaby."

I had a rock-and-roll youth, learned to play piano in high school, meddled in a number of bands, without success. For a while rock and roll was vital and it did the thing I wanted it to do. I wanted to be astonished by music, I wanted to have important certainties of my life called into question by music, I wanted whole civilizations to be founded upon the ominousness of music, and I don't mean that I wanted what particularly good guitar solos do (although these were sometimes nice), or what a good funk band can do (although Funkadelic was great), I mean that I wanted my life changed somehow. I wanted a music that had been passed down through many generations like religious arcana, music that gave access to cabalistic secrets.

There weren't too many records that did this for me, really. But even opening the packaging of *Dolmen Music*, which was one of those moody ECM jackets with the clear plastic sleeve, seemed ritualistic. After I graduated, I took the record with me, or at least a cassette edition of it,

I HAD SUPERSTITIOUS NOTIONS ABOUT WHAT KIND OF MUSIC I WAS SUPPOSED TO LISTEN TO WHILE COMPOSING, AND THIS MUSIC HAD TO BE VERY NARROWLY APPLICABLE TO THE WORKS THEMSELVES.

to California, where I lived for a while in an apartment with the novelist Jeff Eugenides and a theater director called Mark Pleasant. I had only a few cassettes with me in San Francisco, *Dolmen Music* among them, and so I often played Meredith Monk when I wrote. I'm pretty sure it was playing the night of the *earthquake*, which wasn't a big one really. I was working on my Smith-Corona, on some long-lost short story, and the floor of my bedroom looked like it was *rippling* for a second, and there was that cello part, the cello in Just Intonation, that inaugurates the long suite called "Dolmen Music." I ran out into the hall. *Hey, you guys, are you hearing what I'm hearing?*

A few months later I was in Ireland, with my mother, on an ancestral tour, when I saw my first actual dolmen ring. You drove down a certain street, took a left, past a couple of old lorries, walked through some laundry flapping semaphorically in the breeze, and there, in a yard by itself, was this annular arrangement of stones, as in Stonehenge, erected for a purpose now forgotten, but gener-

ous with access to the past, to its losses and jubilances and anxieties—exactly the kinds of things summoned in the song "Dolmen Music," the kinds of things summoned by Meredith Monk's wordlessness, the kinds of things that music has to do and doesn't do enough. One of the first adventures I undertook when I got back after all this traveling was go see Monk perform at Carnegie Hall.

Soon I was in the wilderness of writing my first novel, and then my second, and for both of these books, I had superstitious notions about what kind of music I was supposed to listen to while composing, and this music had to be very narrowly applicable to the works themselves. So, while I was writing *Garden State*, my first novel, I was listening to a lot of Jersey bands, like the Feelies and Yo La Tengo, and other bands associated with the Hoboken sound. With *The Ice Storm*, my obsessions were similarly narrow, except that it was music from the early seventies. In fact, I'd actually started buying records as a kid during those Dark Ages (*Don't Shoot Me I'm Only the Piano*

Player, Led Zeppelin IV, Made in Japan, Dark Side of the Moon), so it was pretty easy to reenact this list. I wasn't listening to much *new music* for a good five or six years, and on the rare occasions when I was it was all Hüsker Dü, the Replacements, the Minutemen, Pere Ubu, and other stalwarts of the indie rock movement.

Until I became bored. Boredom with the popular song, which seems inevitably to overtake you in your late thirties, is a bittersweet thing. It happens incrementally, so it's easy to rationalize or set aside, at first: *This must just be a really bad time for rock and roll*, you say. When a Whitney Houston or a Mariah Carey comes along, you say, *This must just be a really bad time for rock and roll*. When faced with a Sammy Hagar or a Stone Temple Pilots, or a Tool or a Korn or a Live, or any of the whiny Nirvana-imitative, Ritalin-swilling bands of today, you are bored. And you are bored with their bubblegum counterparts, maybe because the melodies just suck, or because the canned electronics sound like car commercials, or because they *are* car commercials, or the hip-hop guys, no matter how important you might think it is giving voice to dis-

enfranchised political groups, the lyrics are about beating on a *ho* or shooting up the place, it's boring. All this stuff stopped speaking to me, see, and maybe it was wrong when younger to believe that my time was epochal, and that all this music was going to transform the world, maybe it was wrong to believe that Sonic Youth was going to change the world, that the best *high-art stuff* and the awesome cultural penetration of popular music were going to meet at some point in the middle, whereupon we would have America realizing how great and creative its artists were instead of churning out the same leaden drum sound in the same leaden fours, saying the same thing over and over; even when I started listening to stuff that most people would consider unlistenable, when I contented myself with heading out onto that promontory of Alvin Lucier and La Monte Young and Terry Riley or Robert Moran or Ingram Marshall or Carl Stone or Stockhausen or Cage or Morton Feldman or Pauline Oliveros, I was still getting older and I still felt like all I was saying was, *Turn down that noise*. I started listening to a lot more vocal music, especially extended-vocal-

BOREDOM WITH THE POPULAR SONG, WHICH SEEMS INEVITABLY TO OVERTAKE YOU IN YOUR LATE THIRTIES, IS A BITTERSWEET THING.

range stuff, like David Hykes, the overtone singer, and Nusrat Fateh Ali Khan and Youssou N'Dour, and Tuvan throat singing, and American sacred-harp singing. Sacred-harp singing was a way to teach church congregations with no organ how to sing hymns. It was big in the South for a long time. It's also called shape note singing, because instead of notating the parts the way you would see them on a G-clef, etc., the specific parts were indicated with little shapes, each for a spot in the old scale *do re mi fa*. As far as I can tell, they didn't even use a pitch pipe to start the sacred-harp pieces, a group leader would just pick a starting note out of thin air. In its primitiveness, sacred-harp singing is some of the loveliest folk music ever made in this country.

All this singing, all this vocal music, led me back to Meredith Monk.

In 1999, a German magazine wanted to know if I could do a dual interview with any artist on earth, who would it be? They had run a series of these features, mostly pretty obvious pairings, actors picking other actors, and so forth, John Turturro and Susan Sarandon. I'm sure they expected me to pick a writer, to pick a William Gass or a Don DeLillo, and these guys are great, of course, and they have helped me a lot by their example and their accomplishments, but since I think of what I do as owing a lot to music, as owing something to singing and

to kinds of improvised rhythms that are very musical, meant to be heard in the ears, instead of seen with the eyes, I wanted to pick a musician, so I picked Meredith Monk.

Naturally, we were being tape-recorded and photographed by a crew of unnecessarily organized German nationals, and after a couple hours of it (the photographs took longer than the interview itself), it was hard to feel much except a sense that Meredith Monk's time was being wasted and that I didn't really deserve the honor of this conversation. It was satisfying to note, however, that Meredith and I had a lot to say about politics for the German magazine, about the hideousness of the Giuliani administration, the hideousness of Tom DeLay, and so forth. Still, I left feeling like I had met a *mahatma*, and that my job was amazing, because it occasioned such opportunities to meet great artists.

Though I believed I had imposed on her more than I wanted to, Meredith made an effort to stay in touch. Which is to say that I kept writing to her, and watching her movies and tapes of her performances and listening to her records, because the records had been made even more impressive by the fact of Meredith's personality, because for all her lovable and approachable warmth as a person, it was still impossible to understand where her talent came from, except that it was *everywhere* in her. I guess it's an impossible question, really, where talent comes from, like that old question about the seat of the soul, it's just there, and you can ask all kinds of questions about the early life of a person like Meredith Monk and talk about the movement-oriented musical program she learned as a child, called Dalcroze Eurythmics, and so forth, but in the end talent just seems impenetrable and awesome.

A strange coincidence was involved with all of this, in that my late sister's name was Meredith too, and she had a monogram pretty close to Meredith Monk's, obviously, since her surname was the same as mine, and I am always acutely aware of friends who are women who are older than I, of not wanting to burden them with the projections of that lost relationship, but one day I was home and playing the messages on the answering machine, sitting on a couch, letting them sing out into my empty house, when a voice said, *Hey, Rick, it's Meredith* . . . At first, everything that came after these words was lost. At first, in my confusion and my disorientation, I thought she was *back*, my sister, as in those Hollywood narratives where you get to experience the dead all over again. Then there was a period of terrible letdown, when I realized it wasn't *her*, though maybe it was, subliminally or emblematically; in some odd kind of way maybe I have admired

Meredith Monk since then, precisely in a sentimental way, because now the unstated message of Monk's phonemic melodies is an injunction to remember.

The story moves toward its crescendo in the second half of 2000, when WNYC asked if I'd like to do something for a Sunday morning show they have called *The Next Big Thing*. I said that I was always looking for ways to work with *music* and musicians, and would it be possible, maybe, to set one of my stories? Some parameters for such a collaboration were discussed, and then they asked me which composer I would like to work with, and I said, without hesitation, *Could we get Meredith Monk?*

What composer doesn't like to get on the radio? That's what I thought, in my naïveté. I mean, I couldn't imagine that she would want to do this thing with me, set my story "Boys," but it's worth dreaming sometimes, right? Meredith agreed to do the piece when the radio station called, but when I talked with her on the phone later on, she admitted, of course, that she was frantically busy, she didn't know if she would have time to do anything new, but I could use the existing recordings as accompaniment for my story, sure. This seemed like generosity enough, especially when it entailed dinner with Meredith. We had a long chat about sustaining creativity, among other things, as she has done for

IT WAS ONE OF THOSE OBSESSIVE TASKS, LIKE IMAGINING WHICH CUTS COULD BE REMOVED FROM THE **WHITE ALBUM**.

almost forty years now, always expanding her range and her investigation. I said lots of things about how her music had changed my life and my work, even though this stuff always feels hollow when you say it. (But I'm writing these lines to "Do You Be" from one of her very first recordings, *Key*, and in the conjunction of the sustained canonical organ chords and the fluttering birdsong soprano vocal line I know I *am* different since I learned of this work.) It was a nice dinner, of the sort I always hoped I'd be having in my epochal youth, and the wait staff at the restaurant, which was right near Meredith's loft, knew her and treated her with incredible reverence. So much so that they actually seemed to think *I* was important, simply because I was with Meredith. Next day, I got an incredible telephone call from Meredith Monk saying that she had gone home and started messing around with her four-track and had already come up with some short pieces, all revolving around the word *boys*.

I recorded the narration first, using a friend, the short-story writer and artist of metaphor, Julia Slavin. Since the story is narrated from the point of view of a *mother* of boys, I wanted a voice that sounded like it understood the material completely. Slavin and I went into the WNYC offices and she banged it out fast. Almost immediately, I had a CD-R version of the recording. Whereupon I went home and, using a computer music program, went about the task of dummying up some of the text with *spot music*, as they do in rough cuts of films, marking where I thought the pauses might go, the silences, the spots where music might play without words of any kind. It was one of those obsessive tasks, like imagining which cuts could be removed from the *White Album*, and it took me several days, chopping up tiny bits of *Dolmen Music* and the two great instrumentals from *Turtle Dreams*, etc., fitting them underneath my words, underneath Slavin's reading, so that my words seemed far more lasting and important than they actually were. I wanted to be prepared when we actually went into the studio with the music and the producers. So that Meredith could do as much as she wanted and no more.

I SOUNDED LIKE WILLIE NELSON ON QUAALUDES.

I'd only been in a digital studio one other time, to record a little piece of *The Ice Storm* for a Little, Brown and Company sales conference. My own voice, which is appalling to me, which I would have surgically altered if there were *cosmetic surgery for voices*, scarcely emerged from the speakers in the studio during the playback. I advised more reverb. *A whole lot more reverb.* Nothing worked. I sounded like Willie Nelson on Quaaludes, and there was nothing to be done about it. Yet my attitude about the studio, left over from analog recording sessions with Jim Lewis when we were in a sequence of bands together in college and graduate school, was pretty much *Record the damn thing and get it over with*, or, as Brian Eno had it, *Honor thy error as a hidden intention.*

Meredith was kind of nervous, I understood later, because of her sometimes complicated relationship to *the studio*, even though she had with her her amazing studio engineer Scott Lehrer. Well, she was *busy* too, and this was not a hugely remunerative gig, of course, for either of us. It was for the fun of it. All the more astonishing then when Meredith Monk went into the proverbial soundproofed booth of the digital recording studio and banged out three separate pieces of music, in two-,

three-, and four-part harmonies with herself, including abstruse time signatures, infrequently visited intervals (the famous *diabla en musica*, or minor second interval), unforgettable melodies, and so forth, in forty-five minutes. It was one of those things that makes clear how the engine of creation is *variety*, variety is *the* manifestation of *possibility*. Meredith Monk has arguably more *possibility* in her, as a singer, than any other singer *has ever had*. Perhaps there have been the likes of Maria Callas or Joni Mitchell or Captain Beefheart who could do particular things better than they had ever been done, but Meredith Monk really is alone in having incorporated *all* the possibilities of the voice into her output, in this way summoning many cultures, many communications, many emotions, some of them fictional, some even imaginary. And she was done with her parts in forty-five minutes.

We went on to fiddle with the rest of "Boys" for five or six hours. At first, my map of how to slug in the music was useful, and a number of my edits (including "Gotham Lullaby" from *Dolmen Music* and "Fat Stream" from *Key*) made it into the final recording, but somewhere around *hour five*, I could see Meredith getting kind of impatient. And since, even though she is incredibly kind and respectful, she never bullshits, she wasn't long about getting to the truth of the situation: *It's starting to get predictable to me. You have the words here and the music here, and the music is abstract and the words aren't.* It was getting late, and Meredith probably had to fly somewhere (she is often on her way to Hong Kong or Copenhagen, or somewhere else interesting), and Dean Olsher, from *The Next Big Thing*, was tired, and in the exhaustion of the moment, it became clear that even though this was one of the most exciting projects I'd ever been involved in, a project that got nearer than I ever had to the kind of music that was in my head when I wrote a sentence, it was still pretty *primitive*, compared to what Meredith was capable of doing, even with something as elemental as a pitch pipe or Jew's harp. By the time I dealt with the force of this conclusion, we were already done, and I was still thinking about it when the show aired on the radio a week later, to some favorable responses. Your life can draw you up to a certain moment, you know, you can see how important a moment it is, and then still wake up and feel like you have a lot more work to do.

Or: All things come to their close,

especially the feeling that your youth was epochal; this feeling comes to an end, the bright eyes of youth are dimmed, all that dancing around to certain soundtracks of youth, it passes away, and you are hurtling from one unfinished task to another and trying to keep creditors at bay. Love letters are horribly outnumbered by bills. It was only a couple of weeks after the collaborative work with Meredith Monk that it seemed like I had never done it at all, it was just some kind of dream I had, a rare alternative to dreams of teaching class without having prepared, which I have a couple of times a month. Now, predictably, I was back to my same long list of failures and inabilities, and this seems like *the situation.* There is no other. My youth was not epochal. I was just vain. And so what's left after? Elegy, requiem, nocturne, lullaby, all the musical idioms of late night? And what is the best instrument for all of these musical idioms? Not the cello, though the cello is splendid, not the harpsichord, though it is good, not the harmonium, though the harmonium is very melancholy and summons the truths of the past. No, the best instrument for the music of loss, which is the best of all music, is a woman's voice. 🔥

THE BEST INSTRUMENT FOR THE MUSIC OF LOSS, WHICH IS THE BEST OF ALL MUSIC, IS **a woman's voice.**

LESSONS

by
C. K. Williams

1.

When I offered to help her and took the arm
of the young blind woman standing
seemingly bewildered on my corner,
she thanked me, disengaged my hand
and tucked one of hers under my elbow
with a forthright, somehow heartening firmness;
we walked a few blocks to the subway
and rode awhile in the same direction;
she studied history, she told me, then here
was my stop, that's all there was time for.

2.

Something about feeling the world
come towards her in irrational jags,
a hundred voices a minute, honks,
squeals, the clicking blur of a bike,
and how she let herself flow across it
with the most valiant, unflinching unsurprise
made the way I dwell in my own cognition,
the junctures of perception and thought,
seem suddenly hectic, blunt,
the sense of abundances squandered, misused.

3.

My first piano teacher was partly blind;
her sister, whom she lived with,

was entirely so: she had a guide dog,
a shepherd, who'd snarl at me from their yard—
I feared him nearly as much as my teacher.
She, of the old school, cool and severe,
because of her sight would seem to *glare* at my fingers,
and she kept a baton on the keyboard to rap them
for their inexhaustible store of wrong notes
and for lags of my always inadequate attention.

4.

Still, to bring her back just to berate her
is unfair, I mustn't have been easy either.
I keep being drawn to that place, though:
there was some scent there, some perfume, some powder;
my ears would ring and my eyes widen and tear.
Rank, wild, it may have been perspiration—
they were poor—or old music, or books;
two women, a dog: despite myself,
stumbling out into the dusk—dear dusk—
I'd find myself trying to breathe it again.

5.

. . . And the way one can find oneself strewn
so inattentively across life, across time.
Those who touch us, those whom we touch,
we hold them or we let them go
as though it were such a small matter.
How even know in truth how much
of mind should be memory, no less
what portion of self should be others
rather than self? Across life, across time,
as though it were such a small matter.

THE DEEP ROOTS OF
Detroit R&B

THE MUSIC IS

What it is. The music.

"Our attachment to it"—Amiri Baraka says in *The Autobiography of LeRoi Jones*—"one deep definition of who we are and where we think we are going."

Deeply defining. The shape of a world. The complex connections within that world.

BY LAWRENCE JOSEPH

"But you really"—

Gertrude Stein writes in "To Americans," the conclusion to *Brewsie and Willie*— "have to learn to express complication." You have to learn how to express complication and go easy, "and if you cant go easy go as easy as you can."

"And they'll lay you down low in the easy": the opening of "Glad Tidings," the final song on Van Morrison's *Moondance*.

So now, you go and you be easy, just go easy, be easy, down into the easy now, be easy, be as easy as you can.

In *P.M. Magazine*, March 11, 1945, Richard Wright reviewed Stein's *Wars I Have Seen*. "But, you might ask, why do I, a Negro, read the allegedly unreadable books of Gertrude Stein? It's all very simple, innocent even." He stumbled on Stein's work, Wright said, "without the guidance of those critics who hint darkly of 'the shock of recognition.' " Prompted by random curiosity while browsing one day in a Chicago public library, he took a tiny volume called *Three Lives* from the shelves and looked at a story in it entitled "Melanctha." "The style was so insistent and original and sang so quaintly that I took the book home." As he read it, his ears were "opened for the first time to the magic of the spoken word. I began to hear the speech of my grandmother, who spoke a deep, pure, Negro dialect and with whom I had lived for many years."

Told that Stein's tortured verbalisms were throttling the revolution, Wright gathered a group of semiliterate black stockyard workers—" 'basic proletarians with the instinct for revolution' (am I quoting right?)"—into a basement and read "Melanctha" out loud to them. They understood, said Wright, every word. "Enthralled, they slapped their thighs, howled, laughed, stomped, and interrupted me constantly to comment on the characters."

Baraka: "We know people by what moves them, what they use as background sounds for their lives, whatever they seem to be. We are talking about feeling and thought, emotion, aesthetics, and philosophy (and science)."

Feeling. Thought. Emotion. Aesthetics. Philosophy. Science. The instinct for form and technique. The instinct for a formal and a technical revolution.

"By the 1960s Middle Eastern and Indian rhythms, scales, instruments, and time signatures were making wide inroads in modern jazz, but in 1957 Lateef was clearly a pioneer in this regard," Lars Bjorn and Jim Gallert note in *Before Motown: A History of Jazz in Detroit, 1920-60* (certain to be a classic). Born Bill Evans in 1920, changing his name after he became a follower of the Ahmadiyya Islamic movement, Yusef Lateef first became interested in Middle Eastern music while he was working in a factory.

"I realized I had to widen my canvas of expression," Lateef told Jim Gallert in an interview, "Meet the Artist," at the Montreux-Detroit Jazz Festival on September 6, 1999. "I spent many hours in the library on Woodward studying the music of other cultures. At this time I was also working at Chrysler's. I met a man from Syria and he asked me if I knew about the rabat. He made me a rabat and Ernie Farrow played it on the recording. I was looking to widen my expression and made bamboo flutes on my own."

Nat Hentoff, in *Downbeat*, January 9, 1957: Detroit had become "a spawning ground . . . for modern jazz. Their blowing here is primarily of a low flame, conversational kind. They fuse and pulse well together with the rhythm section, a finely knit, flowing texture of full-sounding but not overbearing momentum." The Detroit style, according to Roland Hanna, "tells a story. You hear other pianists running notes and changes. But a musician from Detroit makes an effort to arrive at his own story and tell it in his music."

"Woodward Avenue. Big parades. The library, the museum"—Saeeda

So now, you go and you be easy, just go easy, be easy, down into the easy now, be easy, be as easy as you can.

Lateef writes on the jacket of Yusef Lateef's *Detroit: Latitude 42 30—Longitude 83—* "the Toddle House—BEST pecan waffles; cheap . . . Paradise Theatre . . . The old Mirror Ballroom . . . World Stage . . . New Music Society . . . Detroit Symphony . . . Latitude." "Woodward Avenue," one of my favorite tunes on that recording—"Woodward Avenue," and "Belle Isle," and a version of "That Lucky Old Sun"—and oh yes, I almost forgot: "Eastern Market."

When I was ten years old, I used to go to that Toddle House on Woodward and Palmer. My father and my uncle owned a store on John R., a one-way street that ran downtown, one block east of Woodward. If, from the Toddle House, you walked one block east on Palmer to John R., then one block up, there, on the southeast corner of John R. and Hendrie, was Joseph's Market. "The latter half of the 1940s," note Bjorn and Gallert, "saw the development of the 'Street of Music' in two blocks of John R., between Forest and Canfield" (nine to ten blocks south of Hendrie). There's a photograph of the store from that time. Above it, a billboard, "CHEVROLET," with a two-tone-silver-and-white, '57 Chevrolet, "filled with spirit and splendor!" "JOSEPH'S MARKET. MON. TUE. WED. THUR. 9 TO 9. FRI. SAT. 9 TO 11." "YOUR NEIGHBORHOOD GROCER SINCE 1935 FREE PARKING AROUND THE COR-NER." "5770 JOHN R." "BEER. WINE." "DETROIT PACKAGE LIQUOR DEALER." "BAR B. Q. TO TAKE OUT. RIBS. CHICKEN. PEPSI COLA." I'd walk to the Toddle House for lunch. For less than a dollar you could buy a hamburger, BEST fried potatoes, a Coke.

On the corner of the "Street of Music" and Canfield was a "show bar,"

the Flame. "Detroit's premier venue in the 1940s for black musical entertainment had been the Paradise Theatre"—Bjorn and Gallert relate—"but with the opening of the Flame in 1949 and the closing of the Paradise in November 1951, the action moved over to the Flame." The Flame was a solid testing ground for black entertain-ers who wanted to cross over to an adult mass audience. It was similar to the Par-adise in presenting top national acts, but it also gave some room for local talent. "Berry Gordy's sister Gwen"—Bjorn and Gallert continue—"had the photo con-cession at the Flame with camera assis-tance from her sister Anna and two other

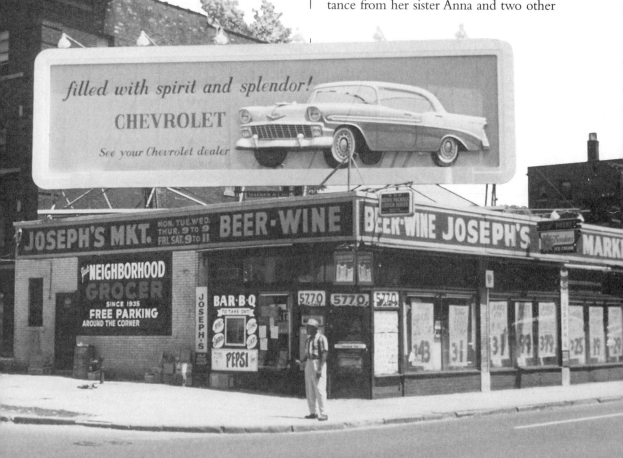

brothers in the darkroom." Among the top national acts: Ella Fitzgerald, Count Basie, Billie Holiday, Dinah Washington, Billy Eckstine ("Jelly, Jelly, Star"), Sarah Vaughan, Erroll Garner. Local talent: Della Reese, Jackie Wilson, Little Willie John, Hank Ballard.

Della Reese, quoted in Arnold Shaw's *The Rockin' 50s*: "The Flame was the place to be. In Detroit, in an area of five to six blocks, there wasn't one without spots of live entertainment. Friday and Saturday nights were get-up-and-go nights, get dressed and go out. But every night was nightclub night. The Flame was the hottest spot in town. The Flame was letting your hair down."

"The Flame was a continuous show, right through the night," Johnny Ray told Shaw. Ray was "the only white guy" who appeared there, but, as far as the club was concerned, the scene was black and tan. The Flame's house band, led by Maurice King, backed Ray on his first two records. Ray's next tune, "Cry," was a number-one hit on both the pop and R&B charts. Many listeners, hearing "Cry" on the radio, assumed that Ray was black. During live performances of the song, Ray, in the middle of singing, would break down in sobs. A band member would come to his aid, helping him back onto his feet.

"I always wanted to be a guitar player and a singer," Bob Dylan, born Robert

Della Reese

Zimmerman in Duluth in 1941, says in the notes to his Biograph collection. "Since I was ten, eleven, or twelve, it was all that interested me. That was the only thing that I did that meant anything, really." "Henrietta" was the first rock and roll record he remembers hearing. Before that he listened a lot to Hank Williams and, before that, Johnny Ray. "He was the first singer whose voice and style, I guess, I totally fell in love with. There was just something about the way he sang [the opening to 'Cry'] 'When your sweetheart sends a letter' that just knocked me out. I loved his style, and wanted to dress like him, too."

Count Basie

On November 22, 1980, at the Fox Warfield Theater in San Francisco, Dylan told the audience that across the lake from Duluth is a town called Detroit. When he was around twelve, he happened to go to Detroit with a friend of his who had relatives there. Though he couldn't remember how, he found himself in a bingo parlor, where, he said, people came to eat and to dance to a dance band. Where he was from, said Dylan, he'd heard mostly country music—Hank Williams, Hank Snow, "all the Hanks"—but the first time that he was face to face with rhythm and blues was in Detroit. He then broke into a wailing gospel rendition of Little Willie John's "Fever."

Baraka: "Flame itself has different colors. The old blues, spirituals, quartets, and rhythm and blues, the jazz and bebop plus the multicolored pop, the identifiable American flying object."

My father, I remember, pulled the car over to the curb on Woodward Avenue in Highland Park—in the background Henry Ford's original assembly plant, used already as a warehouse—a July Sunday afternoon, the sky absorbed by a solid red sun, and told me to listen, to listen closely—he played with the radio dial to get the sound as clear as he could—listen to how beautiful the voice was in the song that was playing: Dinah Washington's rendition of "Harbor Lights."

"I've been writing songs since I was six years old," William "Smokey" Robinson told Bill Dahl for a December 10, 1993, article, "Going to a Go-Go with Smokey Robinson and the Miracles," in *Goldmine*. "My mom and my two sisters played a lot of Sarah Vaughan. I heard all kinds of music in my house. Mostly Sarah Vaughan, Billy Eckstine, Ella Fitzgerald, Count Basie, people like that." Sarah Vaughan, Robinson said, was "probably my favorite vocalist out of all of them. She used to cry her songs. She was like an instrument to me. She just did things with her voice that only she and Ella could do." (Robinson's playmates included the Motor City's first family of gospel, the Franklins—sisters Aretha, Carolyn and Erma among them. . . . By the time he was in fifth grade, Robinson was writing songs and singing songs regularly, forming a vocal quartet in junior high school that included Aretha's brother, Cecil Franklin.) When he was eleven or twelve, Robinson became interested more, he said, "in what they termed then as the R&B music and rock and roll kind of sound." He had five idols: Clyde McPhatter, Nolan Strong, Frankie Lymon, Sam Cooke, and Jackie Wilson. (Prime examples of the R&B rock and roll kind of sound at the time were Nolan Strong and the Diablos' local hit "Mind Over Matter" and Hank Ballard and the Midnighters' top-of-the-charts "Work with Me, Annie." Ballard also wrote, and with the Midnighters recorded, "Finger Poppin' Time," and, later, "The Twist," covered by Chubby Checker.) The "greatest idol" he ever had "as far as an entertainer," Robinson told Dahl, was Jackie Wilson. "The other guys could sing, but Jackie could sing *and* dance *and* entertain."

Replacing Clyde McPhatter, who had followed Billy Ward as lead vocalist of the Dominoes, Wilson (who credited gospel singers as the main influences on his style) helped shape the doo-wop vocal group tradition in which McPhatter had been a pioneer. Wilson's first record, "Reet Petite," was written by Berry Gordy, Gordy's sister Gwen, and Tyran Carlo.

"Reet Petite" never showed on the R&B charts, but went pop, selling a quarter of a million 45s. In *To Be Loved* (the title of Jackie Wilson's first number-one hit, which Gordy also wrote), Gordy tells how, in 1953, he opened, in the Gordy family's building on Farnsworth and St. Antoine (eight or so blocks from Joseph's Market), the 3-D Record Mart. At first, Gordy said, he sold only jazz recordings, but, as time went on, more and more blues. "I finally had to admit to myself blues was in my soul," he said. This probably stemmed from his early exposure to gospel. "There was an honesty about it. It was just as pure and real as jazz. In fact, jazz had its roots in the blues." Ironically, he said, the simplicity that he'd rejected in the blues was the very thing that people related to. Bjorn and Gallert: "Wilson's recordings of 'Reet Petite' and 'To Be Loved' gave Gordy a name, and singers started coming to him for material. One of them was singer/songwriter Smokey Robinson, who was the seventeen-year-old leader of the Matadors (later the Miracles)."

In his liner notes to *Detroit Blues—The Early 1950s* (which includes John Lee Hooker's "House Rent Boogie"), Paul Oliver defines the Detroit blues style. "Often [the Detroit blues musicians] play with strong piano blues and boogie players who—from the days of Will Ezell and Charlie Spand, through to Big Maceo and Floyd Taylor, to Boogie Woogie Red or

Bob Thurman—have been a strong feature in Detroit blues." Drums also feature prominently in Detroit—"socking, hard-hitting, played by a Tom Whitehead, or in primitive imitation by a Washboard Willie." A number of guitarists, like Eddie Kirkland and Eddie Burns, double on harmonica, and can play the organ too, "weaving in with the sax players, who play a bigger part in Detroit blues than in that of Chicago." This complexity of instrumentation, played against steady-beat rhythms, gave birth to "a smoother, more sophisticated music where the instrumental lines were carried by vocal groups against similar rhythm backgrounds, and which borrowed freely from the gospel idioms which also form an important part of the Detroit musical scene."

Bjorn and Gallert: "Gordy decided to form his own record company, and with an eight-hundred-dollar loan from his family, Tamla was born in January 1959." In his November 7, 1959, column in the *Michigan Chronicle*, Bill Lane observed that Gordy was "the first Negro in the city to open a recording studio of any noticeable consequence" when he purchased the for-

Berry Gordy: "The 'feel' was usually the first thing I'd go for. After locking in the drumbeat, I'd hum a line for each musician to start."

mer Gene LeVett photo building on West Grand Boulevard. Bjorn and Gallert: "Gordy christened the new headquarters Hitsville USA and his increased control over the production, distribution, and marketing of music led to a steady flow of hits. Motown's first number-one R&B hit was the Miracles' 'Shop Around' in 1960, and the first number-one pop hit was the Marvelettes' 'Please Mr. Postman' in 1961. The Motown organization grew rapidly and eventually became the largest black-owned enterprise in the nation."

Berry Gordy: "The 'feel' was usually the first thing I'd go for. After locking in the drumbeat, I'd hum a line for each musician to start. Once we got going, we'd usually ad lib all over the place until we got the groove I wanted. Many of these guys came from a jazz background. I understood their instincts to turn things around to their liking, but I also knew what I wanted to hear—commercially. So when they went too far, I'd stop them and stress, 'We gotta get back to the funk—stay in that groove.' " Gordy would make it, he said, as plain as possible. "I would extend my arms a certain distance apart, saying, 'I want to stay between here and there. Do whatever you want but stay in that range—in the pocket.' But between 'here and there' they did all kinds of stuff—always pushing me to the limit and beyond."

William James (with whom both W. E. B. Du Bois and Gertrude Stein studied philosophy at Harvard): "When I say 'Soul,' you need not take me in the ontological sense unless you prefer to." Soul? "Only a succession of fields of consciousness: yet there is found in each field a part, or sub-field, which figures as focal and contains the excitement, and from which, as from a center, the aim seems to be taken. Talking of this part"—James continues—"we involuntarily apply words of perspective to distinguish it from the rest, words like 'here,' 'this,' 'now,' 'mine' or 'me.' " To the other parts are ascribed "the positions 'there,' 'then,' 'that,' 'her,' 'his,' 'it,' 'not me.' " But, says James, "a 'here' can change to a 'there,' and 'there' become a 'here,' and what was 'mine' and what was 'not mine' change their places." What brings such changes about? The way in which the emotional excitement alters.

There: the funk, the groove. Here: in the pocket.

Are you ready?

"When the beat gets the feel, it's hard to get parted"—"you got yours and I got mine": "Monkey Time," written by Chicago's Curtis Mayfield, sung by Major Lance.

"Mickey's Monkey," written by Eddie Holland, Lamont Dozier, and Brian Holland, sung by the Miracles. "When the people see the dancing they begin to sing—lum di lum di lie." Lum di lum di lie—Detroit's Masonic Auditorium, May 1980. Smokey stops and smiles. "We don't know how to spell it, but we sure know how to say it."

Is everybody ready?

In a small yellow circle on the original purple Gordy label: "It's what's in the groove that counts."

John Lee Hooker, "Boogie Chillen' ": "You know it's in 'em and it's just got to come out."

Thursday, December 16, 1965. The Fox Theatre, downtown Detroit. The Motor Town Review. Junior Walker and the All Stars, Martha and the Vandellas, Stevie Wonder, the Temptations, Marvin Gaye. In *Smokey: Inside My Life*, Robinson recollects: "Junior was such a big-sound, stomp-down saxist, once at the Fox he was dancing so hard, he tripped and fell into the orchestra pit. The pit was deep, but Junior was a showman, and he kept playing, his wail growing more distant the farther he fell, until he landed on his feet, his 'Shotgun' still firing." That was the night. We arrived early. Sat in the tenth or eleventh row near the aisle, as close to the stage as we could. "Shotgun"—you know—"shoot 'em before they run." Dig potatoes. Pick tomatoes. Stevie Wonder, fifteen years old, Clarence Paul beside him scatting gospel on Bob Dylan's "Blowin' in the Wind," followed by a long, pure, frenzied expression on the mouth harp. Music. Sweet music. Music everywhere. Swinging, swaying, records playing: "Do you love me / now that I can dance?— The Contours"—the epigraph to Al Young's first book of poems, *Dancing*. "The field open / the whole circle of life / is ours for the jumping into, / we ourselves the way we feel / right now": from Young's poem "Dancing in the Street." Eddie Kendrick's falsetto, a Whitfield-and-Holland song, "The Girl's All Right with Me." "Ain't that peculiar—peculiarity": written and produced by Smokey, on the Tamla label, sung by Marvin Gaye. Later, on the radio, Sam Cooke's "Having a Party," so we stopped the car, opened the doors, and danced slowly on the street.

In his unauthorized biography *Van Morrison: Inarticulate Speech of the Heart*, John Collis reports on Morrison's appearance at the King's Hotel, Newport, South Wales, on October 6, 1993. Morrison began to lecture the audience. "This is not

"We just speeded blues up and called it 'funk' 'cause we knew it was a bad word to a lot of people."

rock, this is not pop," he said. "This is called soul music. So instead of all the motherfucking bastards who say something different, this is what it is." After several attempts to start singing—never getting beyond "I'm a trans-Euro train"—Morrison continued. "I'm talking about soul. I'm a soul singer. I'm more a motherfucking soul singer than some motherfucking motherfucker. I'm a soul singer. I sing soul songs. Blues."

George Clinton, in an interview, "Brother from Another Planet," with Vernon Reid in *Vibe*: "We came from Motown. I always knew that I had been trained as a producer and a writer and there was nothing else like the discipline they had at Motown. Having done that, then we saw Cream and Vanilla Fudge and all of them take the music my mother liked, flip it around and make it loud, and it became cool. We realized that blues was the key to that music. We just speeded blues up and called it 'funk' 'cause we knew it was a bad word to a lot of people."

Van Morrison's *Saint Dominic's Preview*, the first cut: "Jackie Wilson Said (I'm in Heaven When You Smile)." The opening lines: "Jackie Wilson said it was reet petite,

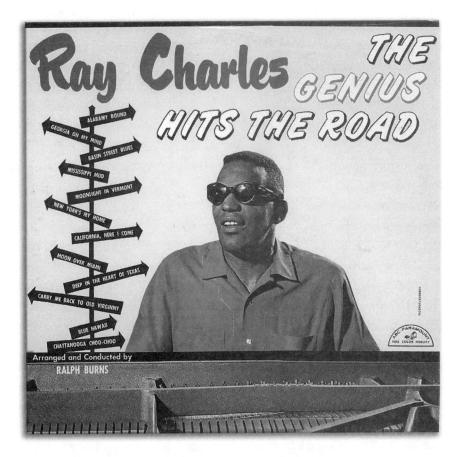

kind of lovin' she gives knocks me off my feet . . ." On *The Healing Game*, the song "Sometimes We Cry," Morrison sings, "Gonna put me in a jacket and take me away, I'm not gonna fake it like Johnny Ray." On *Enlightenment*, in "In the Days before Rock 'n' Roll": "Come in, come in, come in Ray Charles, come in the high priest." "I'm down on my knees at those wireless knobs." Telefunken. Searching for Budapest. AFM. Fats and Elvis, Sonny, Lightnin', Muddy, John Lee, did not come in, no they did not come in, did not come in without those wireless knobs. Soul. Radio. This is the sound of my wavelength and your wavelength—ya radio. You turn me on when you get me on your wavelength—ya radio, ya radio.

"Pulsars, blue receding / quasars—their vibrant / radio waves. Cosmic Ouija, / what is the / mathematics of your message?": the fourth of five parts of Robert Hayden's poem "Stars."

Released in early 1962, Ray Charles's *Modern Sounds in Country and Western Music* remained on Billboard's pop album chart for nearly two years, fourteen weeks in the number-one position. "Not only did it gain him millions of new fans," writes Todd Everett, "the album firmly booted the thirty-one-year-old Charles from the 'r & b' category and let general (let's face it) white audiences know what connoisseurs had taken for granted for several years, that Ray Charles had something to say to virtually everybody and that there's nobody else who can tell it like Brother Ray." The LP's second-to-last cut is "That Lucky Old Sun," according to Everett "a 1949 smash hit by Frankie Laine, written by the Tin Pan Alley tune-smiths Haven Gillespie and Fred Coots."

In a three-day recording session at Blue Rock Studios in New York City in March 1971, Bob Dylan, after recording "When I Paint My Masterpiece," did

covers of "That Lucky Old Sun," Ben E. King's "Spanish Harlem," and the gospel classic "Rock of Ages."

There are those who maintain that Aretha Franklin's version of "Spanish Harlem" ("a rose in *black* and Spanish Harlem") is one of her finest tunes. The June 28, 1968, cover of *Time*: "Singer Aretha Franklin. The Sound of Soul." She was around nine, Franklin recalled, when she decided to sing. Her father was the prominent Detroit clergyman, the Reverend C. L. Franklin. "The best, the greatest, gospel singers came through our home in Detroit. Sometimes they stayed with us. James Cleveland lived with us for a time and it was James who taught me how to play piano by ear." Most of what she learned vocally she learned from her father. "He gave me a sense of timing in music and timing is important in everything." The opening to Bob Dylan's 1966 book *Tarantula*: "aretha / jukebox queen of hymn & him diffused in drunk transfusion wound would heed sweet sound-wave crippled & cry salute to oh great particular el dorado reel." Say what? Sweet soundwave cry salute hymn diffused great particular C-a-d-i-l-l-a-c El Dorado real. Yes, Aretha told *Newsweek* in August '67, she learned a lot from Sam Cooke. "He did so many things with his voice. So gentle one minute, swing-

"Make you wanna holler, the way they do my life, make you wanna holler, the way they do my life, this ain't livin', no, no."

ing the next, then electrifying. Always doing something else." When he was still with the Soul Stirrers, Cooke brought his dub recording of "You Send Me" over to the Franklins' house for the family to hear. "The song became a hit, and Sam went pop." When Cooke made the change, Aretha said to herself, "I'd sure like to sing like that, too."

Soulin' Sam Cooke. "Cherie LP 1001." "Two Record Soul Pack." Written in a small box on the front cover: "BONUS 45 RPM RECORD INSIDE! Never-Before-Heard 25-Minute Rap Session by SAM COOKE 'What is Soul.' " On the back cover: "Dedicated to J. W. Alexander, who knew the true meaning of Gospel Soul Music and became the first to convert it into Rhythm and Blues." Recorded on it, a two-part rendition of Gershwin's "Summertime," each part exactly two minutes, seventeen seconds long.

The desire of truth bursting from within.

Rapping and mapping every generation's survival.

Igniting a brighter and dedicated flame.

The recently released "Deluxe Edition" of Marvin Gaye's *What's Going On.* Two discs. On disc One: "Original LP Release (May 21, 1971)"; "Original Detroit Mix (April 5, 1971)" (previously unreleased); "The Foundation" (" 'What's Going On' rhythm & strings mix") (previously unreleased). On disc Two: "Live at the Kennedy Center (May 1, 1972)"; "Original Single Versions"; "In the

Meantime" ("Head Title aka 'Distant Lover'"). The live performance at the Kennedy Center was Gaye's first in four years. He opened with a medley, the first three songs, "That's the Way Love Is," "You," and "I Heard It through the Grapevine," originally produced by Norman Whitfield. When he recorded for Whitfield, Gaye told David Ritz, "he had me singing so high and hard the veins in my neck nearly popped." After the medley, songs from *What's Going On*. Almost two minutes into "Inner City Blues (Make Me Wanna Holler)," Marvin stops singing and begins conversing, while the band continues to play. "Now Maurice, Maurice King—Maurice King here is my arranger, here, on the piano, and, and, because I want this to be a groovy tune, what I want to do is start all over again from the top, because I want to do it, because we're in the groove now"—the band was still playing—"it's a bit more groovy now, and I want to keep it where it is, from the top, we gonna take it from the *top*, take it from the *top* now . . .

"One, two, three, four, all right, all right, yeah, I got to have it groovy . . .

"Dah dah dah, dah dah dah dah dah dah . . .

"Rockets, moon shots, spend it all on have-nots . . .

"Money we make it, 'fore we see it, you take it . . .

"Make you wanna holler, the way they do my life, make you wanna holler, the way they do my life, this ain't livin', no, no, ain't livin', no, no, no . . ."

Nelson George, in his beautiful elegy "The Power and the Glory," in the *Village Voice*, May 8, 1984: Marvin said he had "three different voices, a falsetto, a gritty gospel shout, and a smooth midrange close to his speaking voice. Depending on the tune's key, tone, and intention, he was able to accommodate it, becoming a creative slave to the music's will."

Marvin's "Trouble Man": "I know some places and I see some faces, got some connections, they dig my directions, what people say, that's okay, they don't bother me—I'm ready to make it, don't care about the weather, don't care about no trouble, I got myself together, I see the protection that's all around me."

Smokey's "A Love She Can Count On" : "I know that you know how precious to care is, and you know, my darling, that I know that there is . . ."

Like sunshine. I got sunshine. You are my sunshine. I feel like this is the beginning, though I've loved you for a million years, and if I thought our love was ending, I'd find myself drowning in my own tears. You are the sunshine. You are the sunshine of my life. That's why I'll always be around.

Phil Spector, on the radio commenting on the Four Tops' "Reach Out": "If you *feeeeel* that you can't *goooooooooonnn* ...": it's black Dylan.

From *The Changing Same (R & B and New Black Music)*, Baraka: "But it is interpretation. The Miracles are spiritual. They sing (and sing about) feeling. Their content is about feeling ... the form is to make feeling, etc. . . . . 'Walk On By,' 'Where Did Our Love Go?' 'What Becomes of the Brokenhearted?' 'The Tracks of My Tears,' high poetry in the final character of their delivery ... A blues which bees older than Ray Charles or Lightnin' Hopkins, for that matter. 'I got to laugh to keep from cryin',' which the Miracles make, 'I got to dance to keep from cryin',' is not only a song but the culture itself. It is finally the same cry, the same people. You really got a hold on me.

As old as our breath here ... James Brown's screams, etc., are more 'radical' than most jazz musicians sound, etc. Certainly his sound is 'further out' than Ornette's."

As old as our breath. The ancient streets. The back streets. Back on the street. The street only knew your name. Back on the street again.

George Clinton answering Vernon Reid's question "How did funk come into being?": "Our show was basically R&B and we got happy and we became, you know, like churchy. And once we experienced what you could do to people just jumping around from the soul to the blues parts of our songs, we realized that nobody could even be our competition, and we didn't have to worry about doing it fast—everybody in the band would tell you that I said it's gonna take fifteen years for this to work."

Space? Marvin: "Funky space. Peaceful space. It's every place" ("A Funky Space Incarnation"). "Time for countdown, please. Give me the countdown, Zack. Here we go, here we go—you ready?"

"One, fun. Two, you. Three, me. Four, more. Five, no jive. Six, no tricks. Seven, we in heaven, eight, everything is straight. Nine, fine. Ten, next week we'll do it again."

From the top. All over again. Back on the top again. From the *top*.

Stevie Wonder's second LP—he was thirteen years old—*Tribute to Uncle Ray*.

John Rockwell's December 26, 1986, review, "Pop: Smokey Robinson in Six-Night Engagement," in the *New York Times*: "But Mr. Robinson has hardly abandoned his falsetto. Instead, he has integrated it ever more seamlessly into his total method of vocal production, so that most of the time, one can't say for sure exactly what the proportion of 'chest tone,' 'head tone,' and falsetto really is. The now-moribund French operatic style of singing that flourished in the nineteenth century called this blending of registers a 'voix mixte,' and Mr. Robinson mixes his registers as well as any singer alive, operatic or otherwise."

Aretha Franklin's first album in seven years, the CD *A Rose Is Still a Rose*. In an interview with Christopher John Farley from "her hometown of Detroit" in *Time*, March 2, 1998: "I'm a very versatile vocalist. That's what I think a singer should be. Whatever it is, I can sing it. I'm not a rock artist. But I've done some rocking. I love the Puffy song ("Never Leave You

Again") on my album. It's very jazzy, very cool, very easy."

Van Morrison, "Queen of the Slipsteam": "There's a dream where the contents are visible. Where the poetic champions compose. Will you breathe not a word of this secrecy and will you still be my special rose?"

Thought. Feeling. Form. Emotion.

A rose in . . .

A bit more groovy, now, right?

A rose is . . .

Two.

Me. You.

Need a shot of rhythm, need a shot of blues. On the side? A little rock and roll just for good measure. Like, you know, when the chill-bumps come up on you. When the hands start to clapping and the fingers start to popping, and your feet want to move around. When the feeling finally gets you . . .

Hey. Hey now. Hey now, go easy now, keep on keep on pushin' easy now, in the easy now, and, if you can't go easy, then just go as easy as you can.

Bob Dylan: Almost Went to See Elvis. Cool Daddy Productions. Made in Egypt. The second cut: Sam Cooke's "Cupid."

Aretha Franklin: "I'm a very versatile vocalist. That's what I think a singer should be. Whatever it is, I can sing it."

I am looking for the Smokey Robinson stuff. That's what I am here looking for. I am here looking for the Smokey Robinson stuff.

Recorded at the Columbia Studios, Nashville, May 1969.

St. Andrew's Hall, Detroit, July 6, 1999. Between versions of "Silvio" and "Man in the Long Black Coat," Dylan pauses and says: "This afternoon I went over to the Motown Museum. I went over to the Motown Museum and went in, and I asked the man there, 'Where's the Smokey Robinson stuff?' And he says to me, 'I don't know where the Smokey Robinson stuff is.' I say, 'Say what? You don't know where the Smokey Robinson stuff is?' 'No,' he says, 'I don't know where the Smokey Robinson stuff is.' 'Well,' I say, 'that's why I'm here. That is what I am looking for, the Smokey Robinson stuff. That's what I am here looking for. I am here looking for the Smokey Robinson stuff.'"

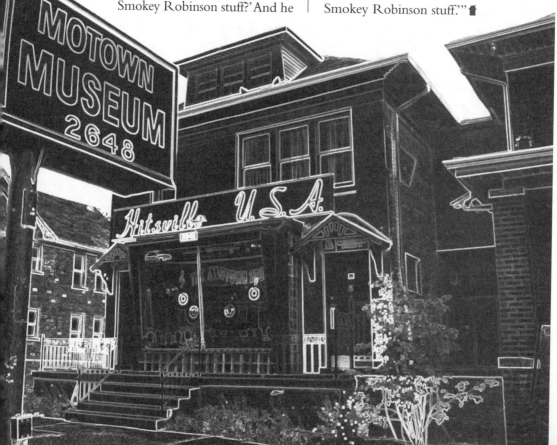

Poetry DJ

by
Julio Marzán

Okay, crew, a REAL poet
just bopped into your face
'cause that Milton man is KING,
so another round for Johhhnnnny MMMMMM!
Now don't forget next week
that Raven' Bronx whole pint
whose name's half P–O–E–try
flashes his tin-tin-a-bulation
nose to nose with Emmy D.
That's right, a polysyllabic slam!
Frenchified metered madness
meets WASP incisor consonants!
So come alone or come enjambed, then smoke
your own poems in the open mike.
Next up the word Zen master,
the word construction worker,
the verbal mojo most quoted
so Bartlett's won't look anorexic,
that iambic pentajazzmeter
whose mama was a sonnet
and whose papa kept a muse!
Pound those palms and show your ghost for
WILLIE SHAKE-IT-SPEARE!!!!!

LINER NOTE

[BY]

JONATHAN LETHEM

BOTHERED BLUE ONCE MORE:
The Barrett Rude Jr. *and* the Subtle Distinctions Story
[2 CDs]

NOTES BY D. EBDUS

The singer's role is deceptive; in identifying and exploring disintegration and other potentially destructive aspects of black American life he or she is performing an integrative function . . . the sense of identity is built not only into the performer-audience relationship . . . but into the very relationships between the sounds he or she makes—the musical techniques themselves."

—*CHRISTOPHER SMALL,* Music of the Common Tongue

People don't recognize the importance of call-and-response. This is because most songs are now written by the people who plan to sing them, and for them the picture is normally complete when they're in it. But a listener likes more than this. The backing vocals, the response, are the voices of society: whether gossiping (as in "Is she really going out with him?") or affirming (as in "Amen!" and "Yeah, yeah, yeah") . . . I would like to do a systematic study of hit songs over the last 30 years. I am sure that at least 80% of them have second vocals in some form or another. But I would bet that not 30% of all recorded songs use backing vocals . . .

—*BRIAN ENO,* A Year, With Swollen Appendices

They created this 'dum-dum-dum' and put me in the middle, and it was like, oh, what is this? I knew it was something different, especially for blacks—you heard rhythm in black records, you didn't hear all this tympani . . . but I was nice in the middle of it. I felt good, maybe because I was too scared to feel any other way.

—*BEN E. KING, on recording "Stand by Me"*

Voices in memory you can't name, rich with unresolved yearning: a song you once leaned toward for an instant on the radio before finding it mawkish, embarrassing, overlush. Maybe the song knew something you didn't yet, something you weren't necessarily ready to learn from the radio. So, for you at least, the song is lost. By chance it goes unheard for fifteen years, until the day when your own heartbreak unexpectedly finds its due date. This happens the moment the song takes you by surprise, trickling from some car radio or airplane headset, to retie the frayed laces of your years. Beguiled from resistance, you permit yourself to hear. But the disc jockey flubs or omits the call list, never names the singer. Or maybe it happens in a movie theater, over a montage which draws unlikely power from the battery of the old song. Afterwards you scan the credits, but fifteen or twenty licensing permissions go by in a blur, hopeless.

So you forget the song again. Or recall just the hook, a dumb central phrase which sours in memory. How could it ever have seemed bittersweet as your own lost youth? How foolish to credit one with the force of the other. Of course, what's missing in your recollection is the cushion of vocal harmony the lead voice floated in on, and that odd sparkle of keyboard effects, and the wash of strings, the fuzzy mumble of bass guitar, the *groove*, all so dated, so perfect. What's missing as well is the story, the context, the space the song lived in. Not to mention any chance for you to make it your own, a chance to spend, say, $34.99 on a two CD set. Instead, half motivated to recapture that feeling, half to console it away, you reach for your time-tested Aretha Franklin, or for *The Best of Motown*, or, forgive us all, some contemporary anodyne, the Fugees or Jamiroquai. That's okay. No one's harmed if you never follow the trail. In an uncertain world it's a reasonable certainty this forgotten song needs you even less than you need it.

Right?

The uppermost pantheon of male soul vocalists—Sam Cooke, Otis Redding, Marvin Gaye, and Al Green (you add your names to those four, I'll add mine)—has a shadow. Indeed, a few shadows, but the one I want to invoke is the one covering those deserving others who fell short of that pantheon. They gather, more or less, in two categories. The first are those denied by the vagaries of luck or temperament—

Howard Tate and James Carr, maybe Arthur Alexander or O. V. Wright. The singers who record for a few different labels, cut a classic A-side or two, then bag out, vanish, drift away. According to the "great man" theory of soul, these are the also-rans.

The second category is the singer disguised within the fame and achievement of a group. Ben E. King of the Drifters, David Ruffin of the Temptations, Levi Stubbs of the Four Tops, Philippe Wynne of the Spinners: all known by their peers as among the finest vocalists ever to step to the mike, known by name. The world knows them only by ear. Though no consolation to a singer in the throes of a frustrated solo career, fighting to claim for himself the wide audience he'd won for his former group, it's worth noting that the singer-group dynamic recapitulates the tensions embodied in a close listener's relationship to a great soul vocal: *Where did this voice come from? What's it straining against? Where can it go next?*

Barrett Rude Jr. is one of the most elusive and singular figures in pop music history. Though none with ears needs telling—if you're reading the booklet, play the damn CDs already!—I'll say it anyway: he's also one of the greatest soul singers who ever lived, not merely one of the best who never got his due. Born in Raleigh, North Carolina, in 1938, Rude was the only child of a troubled marriage, his father an itinerant Pentecostalist preacher-con man (and eventual convict), his mother dying in her late twenties ("of a broken heart," Rude told *Cash Box* magazine in 1972). His musical experience is frequently exaggerated: he sang in his father's church, yes—but Rude's father had his pastorship stripped from him before the future singer was eleven years old, and a year later was in prison. Raised by his aunt, Rude dropped out of high school and migrated from Raleigh to Memphis, where he worked as a janitor, a school bus driver, then, briefly, as a night-owl disc jockey, specializing in blues and jazz, at Memphis radio station KCTO. There he met Junie Kwarsh, the daughter of the station's white owner, who'd been working as a secretary in the station's offices. Rude and Kwarsh quickly married and had a child—unless it was the other way around.

In 1967, at age twenty-nine, Rude recorded a pair of singles at Willie Mitchell's Hi Studio. No one recalls how he came to the studio's attention—Rude always denied that his father-in-law had arranged the opportunity. In 1967 Hi was still treading water with instrumentals and novelty cuts, while producer Mitchell, with singer O. V. Wright, had begun exploring the sweet, deep-bottomed groove he'd soon exploit so masterfully with Al Green. Maybe Rude could have stepped into Al Green's shoes in advance and altered pop history—the evidence is here in four cuts, including the pulsing, horn-driven soul-funk of "Set a Place at Your Table," which briefly touched the R&B charts in February of 1967, and the slowed-down, eerily sexy Hank Williams cover "I Saw the Light." But it wasn't to be. Cultivating a reputation as an eccentric who pinballed between flamboyance and brooding, Rude was dismissed as intractable by the even-tempered Mitchell before his late-blooming career had even begun.

Rude was seemingly on his way to the first kind of story—the handful of cult singles—until the day in February 1968, in a Philadelphia rehearsal studio, when a session guitarist named Marv Brown, who'd played at Hi Records a year before, suggested his name to a road-worn, journeyman vocal group known then as the Four Distinctions. The group had signed a management deal and were rehearsing under the hand of a young producer named Andre Deehorn. Deehorn had a sheaf of songs he imagined could be hits for a harmony-and-lead group. What he had in the Distinctions was harmony without the lead.

> DEMONS WERE NEVER FAR AT BAY IN A CAREER VEXED BY SMOLDERING RAGES, OPAQUE WHIMS, AND UNCANNY DISAPPEARANCES FROM STUDIO AND STAGE DATES.

Brown thought he knew the singer they were looking for, a fellow who'd bottomed out in Memphis and was driving a bus in Raleigh, North Carolina—where, with his young wife and child, Rude had retreated to live with his aunt. Marv's recommendation cut enough ice that a call was made, no matter that there might be a dozen unemployed singers in Philadelphia. No matter that Rude had proved difficult. Perhaps Brown, who'd been fired at around the same time, held a grudge on Rude's behalf. Rude bought a Greyhound ticket and came in for an audition.

Unknown at thirty, Rude might have seemed a dark horse for pop immortality. Demons were never far at bay in a career vexed by smoldering rages, opaque whims, and uncanny disappearances from studio and stage dates. Safe guess that among his woes an unhappy interracial marriage was a formidable cross to bear in sixties mid-America. His recording career spans just a decade; Rude was silenced by drug abuse and domestic tragedy at the end of the seventies.

Nevertheless, from the moment he walked into the Philadelphia studio, Barrett Rude Jr. was destined to be a singer of the second type: the secret, soaring voice contained—and sometimes uncontained—within a famous harmony group. Assuming the "great man" theory of soul tells a lie (and certainly it doesn't tell enough of the truth), then Rude had in the Distinctions found the context in which he could tell the story he had to tell, a place to do the one thing a human being can hope to do— matter for a while. If he regarded it as something like a prison, we can only respectfully disagree, and be grateful that his was an art built on dramas of confinement and escape.

But who were these four men that I'm selling to you here as *a cushion, a context, a containment* for Barrett Rude Jr.? The Distinctions began as friends, working-class black teenagers in the era of Johnny Ace and Jackie Robinson, growing up in the Henry Ford-named and -designed industrial suburb of Inkster, Michigan (also home to the Marvelettes). James Macy, Dennis Longham, Rudolph Bicycle (his real name, all sources agree), and Alfred Maddox were a quartet before they were a singing group, forming the all-black infield of the Dearborn-Inkster Chryslers, an early integrated high school team which won a controversial state championship in 1958. That after they switched from ball to doo-wop it was the shortstop, Jimmy Macy, who sang bass and the first baseman, Rudy Bicycle, who handled the tenor leads, stands only as further evidence that pop truth is stranger than fiction. Baritones Fred Maddox and Denny Longham ranged between Macy's lows and Bicycle's highs (and are nearly indistinguishable on record). The Chrystones, as they were first known, were a resolutely secular group, and it was only a year later that Longham pointed out to the others the misleading resonance of their name, and suggested an alternative: the Four Distinctions. Under that name the teenage group would go on to play school dances, state fairs, storefront church weddings, and yes, baseball games.

In May 1961, the Four Distinctions coughed up a fifty-dollar entrance fee for the privilege of winning a sing-off sponsored by Jeromy Baltwood's notorious Tallhat label. Their prize was a pair of sessions. Who penned the four numbers cut in Tallhat's storefront studio that summer? Though it's probable the Distinctions walked in with the songs, anything beyond J. Baltwood's songwriter credit is lost to the misty veils of time. Included here are "Hello" and "Baby on the Moon," the first a lovely doo-wop plaint, the latter a Five Royales-style vamp. Neither charted, on this world or the moon.

In 1965, Tallhat's stable was bought out by Motown, but at the bigger company the group met with only frustration. Fourth or fifth in line for songs behind the Four Tops, the Temptations, and a host of other aspirants, the Distinctions found themselves singing backup, running errands, answering telephones, and fetching star acts back and forth from the airport. Denny Longham even learned to cut and process hair; he was reputed by Martha Reeves to give "the best conk in town." They did, however, come as near to glory as "Ain't Too Proud to Beg," the same Norman Whitfield production the Temptations would soon ride to the Top 10. Rudy Bicycle's lighter-than-air falsetto version was suppressed in favor of the senior group, but not before a B-side was prepared. "Rolling Downhill" might have seemed to describe the group's plight in Berry Gordy's organization; in fact it's a lost gem of a Holland-Dozier-Holland ballad. Career rescue would come later, in the form of Andre Deehorn, Marv Brown, and Barrett Rude Jr., and it would be three more years before Deehorn added "Subtle" to their moniker. But the Motown tracks are all the proof needed that the Distinctions before Rude were subtle, and polished, with a habit of making the hard plays look easy. Like a lot of prodigies, in baseball or music, Maddox, Longham, Bicycle and Macy became consummate professionals rather than geniuses. No shame there.

DENNY LONGHAM EVEN LEARNED TO CUT AND PROCESS HAIR; HE WAS REPUTED BY MARTHA REEVES TO GIVE "THE BEST CONK IN TOWN."

From Gerald Early's *One Nation Under A Groove: Motown and American Culture:* "The three major early groups of the company—the Supremes, the Temptations, and the Miracles—were put together and rehearsed at their high schools. They were not church groups . . . and in various autobiographies there is little talk about the influence of the black church in their music . . ." This is a useful correction, but stops a little short. The emotionally overreaching, frame-breaking sound that defines soul is epitomized by the configuration the Subtle Distinctions fell into once Barrett Rude Jr. signed on: a Detroit or "northern"-style high school harmony group fronted by a rougher, churchified, "southern"-style lead. This collision of grit and elegance, of raw R&B lust and repentance with polished, crossover-seeking pop is also the crossroads where sufferation and exile briefly join hands with new-glimpsed possibilities of middle-class striving and conformity. The results are, well, about what you'd expect from sounds (and meanings) trying to hold hands while walking different ways down a crossroad. Paradoxical. Poignant. Not a permanent arrangement.

Take for example the Drifters' 1959 "There Goes My Baby," seen by some as the definitive moment when R&B turned to the possibility of another music called soul. Lead singer Ben E. King's strangled vocal, a sort of free-verse bleat of despair (he was pushed to sing in the wrong key) is pinned between a vaguely Latin beat and mock-classical strings. Though it sounds like an iconic "oldie" to us now, the results at the time not only horrified the record label, which nearly refused to release it, but puzzled the song's producer, Jerry Leiber, who said, "I'd be listening to the radio sometimes and hear it and I was convinced it sounded like two stations playing one thing." This drama was reenacted in James Brown's strings-and-shrieks ballads like "Bewildered" and "It's a Man's, Man's Man's World," as well as in the treacly arrangments which dogged the recording careers of moaner-shouters like Jackie Wilson and Solomon Burke.

What's remarkable isn't that fifties song structures were inadequate to those unfettered soul voices just then locating their force. What's remarkable is how sixties soul produced at black-run companies like Motown, Vee-Jay, and Stax created an entire language based on the play of such voices in inadequate or mock-inadequate containers. Drama was enacted by a confinement of strings or horns, but also by lyrics—innumerable soul crescendos occur in covers of apparently corny, 'white' material, Marvin Gaye's "Yesterday," Otis Redding's "Try a Little Tenderness" and Al Green's "How Can You Mend a Broken Heart" being just a few examples.

Drama took its purest form, though, in the vocal interplay developed in the laboratory of groups like the Soul Stirrers, the Five Blind Boys of Alabama, and the Five Royales, as well as in a thousand doo-wop stairwells—voices rattling in a cage of echoes, or shaking off a straitjacket of rhyme, or outrunning escalating platforms of harmony which threaten to engulf it. That's where the Distinctions come in. The Philadelphia production style within which they cut their great records revived the smoothest of doo-wop harmonizing styles to suit a new sophistication of recording technique. Producers like Thom Bell and the team of Gamble and Huff raised the game of containment to the next level, so singers like the Blue Notes' Teddy Pendergrass and the O'Jays' Eddie Levert had to find every possible way not only to shout, grunt and plead their way out of the traps devised, but to murmur, chortle, whisper, and soar in falsetto as well.

In this game no one set traps like Deehorn and the Distinctions, and no one slipped them like Rude. Hear it first in the spring 1978 demo recordings which secured the Distinctions' deal with Philly Grove: a sketch of their first chart hit, "Step

Up and Love Me." With Deehorn's production scheme still an incomplete sketch, the nearly a cappella voices weave a nest for Rude's whispery intro, then push it out into soaring flight. From the same sessions comes the previously unreleased debut of Rude's songcraft, "So-Called Friends."

The new group was installed at Sigma Sound studios to record a full album. Rude, who'd been sleeping on Marv Brown's couch, bought a house and sent for his wife and child, who'd been waiting in North Carolina; the new career was under way. On the debut, the strings-drenched *Have You Heard the Distinctions?*, Deehorn's warm, appealing love songs and his lush, aching productions dominate proceedings—here was the group worthy of his surefire hits. His arrangement of "Step Up and Love Me," complete with flugelhorn and glockenspiel, established the group's chart viability, smashing through to #1 on the R&B charts while attaining #8 pop. Rude was given a co-credit on the wrenching "Heart and Five Fingers," though it's hard to imagine his cajoling, sobbing outro was ever actually written down. When tour promoters at last began ringing the phone, the group was ready; they'd only been practicing their footwork for a decade.

Apprenticeship was past. Atlantic Records purchased the smaller label's contract and returned the team to Sigma to cut their first masterpiece, *The Deceptively Simple Sounds of the Subtle Distinctions*. The classic "(No Way to Help You) Ease Your Mind" inaugurated a brief songwriting partnership between Deehorn, Rude, and guitarist Brown. With "Happy Talk" and "Raining on a Sunny Day" also reaching the charts, if you owned a radio, Rude's aching falsetto and the Distinctions' rich, percolating harmonies dominated the summer of '70. Beyond only hits, the album was a banquet of elegant contemporary moods, the group at the summit of their early form, best described by Dave Marsh in his *Heart of Rock & Soul*: "Pure déjà vu, seeming to call up feelings of nostalgia for a doo-wop soul that had never actually existed." Though it may seem inevitable that the tone would darken, at the time it was easy to wish for summer to last forever—or for a hundred albums as lovely as *Deceptively Simple Sounds*. Instead we have just one.

Taking a cue from Curtis Mayfield in "Move On Up," Marvin Gaye in "What's Going On" (and just about every other soul singer living in the Ball of Confusion that was the new decade), the Subtle Distinctions recorded their socially conscious *In Your Neighborhood* in the fall of 1971. With a cover photo of the group in a vacant lot warming their hands over an oil-drum fire, the album was rushed into stores before Christmas by an A&R office fearful the appetite for conscience might peter out. No fear—*Superfly* was right around the corner—but the look didn't fit the group, and *Neighborhood* was no Christmas record. Rude delivered corruscating vocals on his own "Sucker Punches" (which reached #18 R&B while failing to dent the pop charts), "Jane On Tuesday," and "Bricks In the Yard," but the album bombed. In the dubious tradition of 100 Proof Aged in Soul's "I'd Rather Fight Than Switch," Marvin Gaye and Tammi Terrell's "Ain't Nothing Like the Real Thing" and other Madison Avenue-inspired tunes, Deehorn's "Silly Girl (Love Is for Kids)" nudged to #11 R&B, #16 pop, providing some tonal—and chart—relief.

Redemption was sweet indeed: *Nobody And His Brother* was less a retreat than a recasting of the darkness of *Neighborhood* in deeper, more personal terms, made possible by Rude's assertion of songwriting leadership. "Bothered Blue" was an immediate #1, topping both charts in October 1972, and if it's the only song you were certain you knew when you purchased this set, you're forgiven. Listen again. The song is better, more heartrending and true with each passing year, one of the most *grownup* testaments of

THE SONG IS ONE OF THE MOST GROWNUP TESTAMENTS OF AMBIVALENCE AND ENNUI EVER TO BE TURNED INTO THE BACKDROP FOR A BURGER KING COMMERCIAL.

ambivalence and ennui ever to be turned into the backdrop for a Burger King commercial. Album tracks like "The Lisa Story," "If You Held the Key," and "Grown Up Wrong" form a war for the band's allegiance with co-writer Deehorn—Rude's voice and lyrics raging against the placid, normative formats Deehorn throws in his path, while Maddox, Longham, Macy and Bicycle try desperately to play peacemakers, to give harmonic soothing to the lead voice burning in the foreground. When Rude flies they offer a landing pad, when he stumbles they pull him to his feet, when at last he needs to sleep they tuck him in. Only "Bothered Blue" charted, but that was all it took for the album to find its place and become their number-one seller.

Rude quit the group with the song still on the charts. The Distinctions' last album, *Love You More!* is a retroactive construct, Deehorn's weavings-together of a shambles of song fragments and rehearsal tapes Rude left in his wake. The catchy, understated "Painting of a Fool" was a brief R&B hit in June 1973, but the album fooled no one. The Distinctions were dropped from Atlantic, and quickly parted ways with Deehorn, who had some disco fish to fry. The group slipped quickly and easily into an afterlife on the dinner-club oldies circuit, seemingly as reluctant to completely retire the name as they were to sully it by recording without Rude up front. Few retire as gracefully—call them soul's Sandy Koufax.

As for the departure of the irreplaceable, erratic, and beloved Rude, no one was pleased, and no one was surprised. His studio battles with Deehorn were a legend, and for good reason. Black pop was headed in another direction, "Bothered Blue" notwithstanding. Deehorn would produce many hits in next years, but the place of a Barrett Rude Jr. was far from certain. For every soul shouter like Johnnie Taylor, who, with "Disco Lady," found career revival, were dozens who'd come to the end of the road. But if the too-slick rhythm of the uptempo Philly numbers anticipated (and helped create) disco, that only adds a poignance to what became, in the sound of the Spinners, Manhattans, Blue Notes, Delfonics, Stylistics, and Subtle Distinctions, classic soul's last burst.

> MARVIN GAYE IS SOUL'S PARADIGMATIC FIGURE, CARRYING HIS CONFINEMENTS ANYWHERE, EMBEDDED IN HIS VOICE ITSELF.

It should be added, though, that the music which replaced soul wasn't only disco. It's hard to describe what changed in Stevie Wonder's records once he began playing all the instruments, except that it doesn't *feel* like soul—more like the most humane pop-funk ever recorded. By bringing the music into full accord, Wonder outgrew the paradoxes. Similarly, Al Green's late-seventies gospel is fine stuff, but after he abandoned Willie Mitchell and the house band at Hi, the music no longer teetered between worlds. Rap, funk, disco, and contemporary R&B, though sourced in soul, tend to resolve or abandon the tension. The counterexample is Marvin Gaye, who, when he began arranging his own material, waded even deeper into the unresolvable. Gaye is soul's paradigmatic figure, carrying his confinements anywhere, embedded in his voice itself.

Could Barrett Rude Jr. have carried on with something like Gaye's force through the seventies? Maybe. He tried. He failed. Rude was never a confident songwriter—all but two of his Distinctions songs carry Deehorn's or Brown's name as collaborator. Record buyers and radio programmers knew his voice but not his name: he might sing "Bothered Blue" on stage until he was bothered gray, but he couldn't record it again. At thirty-four, he was starting over. 1972's *On His Own* shouldn't have been a bad start: with Marv Brown in tow as collaborator and arranger, Rude recorded a dreamy suite of love songs as intimate as notebook jottings, using many of the personnel from the Sigma sessions. Unbilled, the Distinctions sang backup on two numbers, "This Eagle's Flown" and the sole hit, "As I Quietly Walk," which lodged comfortably at #12 on the R&B charts but couldn't rescue the album from public indifference (and, Rude claimed, corporate sabotage on the part of Andre Deehorn).

We tend to turn away when ballplayers sign with new teams, when child actors grow older, when groups break up and their members go solo. Still, in Rude's view the Distinctions represented a kind of infancy, the solo career his long-delayed adulthood. The non-reception of *On His Own* was bitter. Increasingly isolated from the advice of friends, Rude divorced Junie Kwarsh and moved to New York. His last album, *Take It, Baby*, treats the split with agonized specificity—the million-dollar contract he'd bargained on leaving the Distinctions had been turned over in a divorce settlement. Eschewing Atlantic's resources, and leaving behind even Marv Brown, Rude recorded at the New Jersey studios of Sylvia Robinson, formerly of Ian & Sylvia ("Love Is Strange") fame, later the godmother of the Sugarhill rappers. The result is a tour de force of unleashed resentment—whispered, growled, and bellowed—and nearly unlistenable by the standards the Distinctions' audience had come to expect. "Lover Of Women" and "Careless" more or less succeed out of context; the latter briefly visited the R&B charts. "A Boy Is Crying" alludes to a custody battle, but from the sound might be a battle between Rude's two or three selves, among which there are only losers.

Rude's last, stray single, "Who's Callin' Me?" recorded and released in 1975, is a confession of paranoiac retreat in the form of a string of guesses at the identity of a caller; a ringing telephone is audible through the seething funk. *"A bill collector?"* Rude wonders. *"Can't be my brother, my brother never calls."* After considering *"A wrong number/Some unwed mother/my last producer/a slick seducer/a mob enforcer"* and others, just barely heard on the fadeout is a last, anguished possibility: *"Is it my mean old father, callin' me?"* In light of later events the coincidence is eerie and jarring. The B-side, "Crib Jam," is a vacancy: Rude's voice and handclaps are heard on the margins, exhorting the vamping band.

Rude's last visit to the recording studio, and last stab at the charts, was in 1978 as a guest vocalist on Dufus Funkstrong's "(Did You Press Your) Bump Suit (single edit)", a twenty-minute funk jam boiled down for release as a hopeless single. It touched the charts, but didn't stick. Rude's vocal aeronautics never sounded better and—unmoored from structure or sense by goonish lyrics and sprawling music—never meant less. An even odder epilogue is provided by two examples of privately recorded four-track demos, probably circa 1977-79. "Smile Around Your Cigarette" and "It's Raining Teeth" are each haunting and disjointed compositions, and each beautifully if lazily sung, suggesting the influence of Sly Stone. Rude was smashed on cocaine at the time.

I promised a story, and stories have endings, however much we might wish to avoid them. Never knowing the name of the singers whose songs stir us is knowing too little; tracing their lives to the last chapter, it seems possible to know too much. But from Bix Beiderbecke to Little Willie John, Sam Cooke, and beyond, we've invited the sorrows of biographical fact to become inextricable from the force of art—there's no reason to make Rude and the Distinctions the exception. If I can't sort out the ache in his voice from what I know, why should you be any different? Who or what, really, is there to protect?

> STORIES HAVE ENDINGS, HOWEVER MUCH WE MIGHT WISH TO AVOID THEM. NEVER KNOWING THE NAME OF THE SINGERS WHOSE SONGS STIR US IS KNOWING TOO LITTLE; TRACING THEIR LIVES TO THE LAST CHAPTER, IT SEEMS POSSIBLE TO KNOW TOO MUCH.

Andre Deehorn produced a variety of acts in Philadelphia and later in Los Angeles, scoring on the dance charts with Vandy Brice, Sophistifunction, and Fool's Gold, among others. He now works as a personal manager in Los Angeles. Rudy Bicycle and Alfred Maddox are happy men and lifelong friends, each living with their families in Dearborn, Michigan, each working in the industry which has supported them all their lives, Bicycle booking musical acts at casinos in nearby Windsor, Ontario, and Maddox, ironically, as a publicist for the Motown Museum. With a couple of younger singers—one a pretty fair Barrett Rude Jr. imitator—they'll occasionally reunite under the Distinctions name and perform the early hits, if the mood strikes and the fee is right.

Denny Longham never lost his interest in hair; after the Distinctions disbanded in 1977 he opened *King's Hair Throne*, a clip shop in South Philly, and was a neighborhood fixture until his death from pneumonia in 1985. He was forty-four. In

1977 James Macy followed Andre Deehorn to Los Angeles—from that vantage in time disco may have appeared a bottomless well of fortune—and struggled for years to find a hit on a variety of distaff labels. He and two companions were killed by shotgun blasts by unknown assailants while sitting in a car at a traffic light in Culver City on September 25, 1988. He was forty-seven. Marv Brown never again found a musical partnership as satisfying as that which began at the Hi Studio in 1967. He worked with the house band at Sigma for a year, then vanished, and later took his own life by hanging in a Patterson, New Jersey, flophouse in 1994. He was fifty-six.

After winning custody of his son, Barrett Rude Jr. moved to Brooklyn, and there sank gradually into a cocaine-fueled desolation. Rude's father joined the household after his release from prison in 1977, and his relationship with Rude was uneasy at best. The atmosphere was volatile, a mixture of Rude's hedonism and indolence and his father's quirky brand of Pentecostalism, with its moral fervor, its love-hate fascination with music and sensuality, its arcane Sabbath days. (It's odd to consider that Marvin Gaye, Philippe Wynne, and Barrett Rude Jr. were all, by choice or upbringing, not merely religious but *weird black Jews*.) On August 19, 1981, during a family dispute, Barrett Rude Sr. aimed a pistol at his son and grandson. Whether he intended to use it can't be known. Another gun appeared; grandson shot grandfather to death. Rude's son, who'd turned eighteen six months before, was convicted of involuntary manslaughter. Neither handgun in the incident was registered; both likely belonged to Rude. Though he was uninjured, the gunshot ended what remained of Rude's public life. His silence since that time is complete. For what it's worth, the man is still alive.

That's the story. But what matters is a story in song. The music on this collection tells a tale—of beauty, inspiration, and pain—in voices out of the ghetto and the suburb, the church and the schoolyard, voices of celebration and mourning, sometimes voices of pensiveness and heartache so profound they feel unsustainable in the medium of pop. The voices may propel you to warble along or to dance; they may inspire you to seduction or insurrection or introspection or merely to watching a little less television. The voices of Barrett Rude Jr. and the Subtle Distinctions lead nowhere, though, if not back to your own neighborhood. To the street where you live. To things you left behind.

And *that's* what you need, what you needed all along. Like the song says: Sometimes we all must get bothered blue.

DISC ONE tracks 1-2 The Four Distinctions, singles on Tallhat, 1962; "Hello," "Baby On the Moon." 3-4 The Four Distinctions, cancelled Tamla single, 1964 "Ain't Too Proud to Beg" b/w "Rolling Downhill." 4-8 BRJ, singles on Hi, 1967: "Set a Place at Your Table" (R&B #49 /, pop/), "Love in Time," "Rule of Three," "I Saw the Light." 9-10 unreleased demos, 1968: "Step Up and Love Me," "So-Called Friends." 11-14 from Have You Met the Distinctions? Philly Groove, 1969: "Step Up and Love Me" (R&B #1, Pop #8), "Eye of the Beholder," "Heart and Five Fingers," "Lonely and Alone." 15-19 from The Deceptively Simple Sounds of the Subtle Distinctions, Atco, 1970: "(No Way to Help You) Ease Your Mind" (R&B #1, eight weeks, Pop #2), "Far More the Man," "Raining on a Sunny Day" (R&B #7, Pop #88), "Happy Talk" (R&B #20, Pop #34), "Just in Case (You Turn Around)." DISC TWO 1-4 from /The Distinctions/ In Your Neighborhood, Atco, 1971: "Sucker Punches" (R&B #18 /, pop, did not chart/), "Silly Girl (Love Is for Kids)" (R&B #11, Pop #16), "Jane On Tuesday," "Bricks in the Yard." 5-9 from Nobody and His Brother, Atco, 1972: "Bothered Blue" (R&B #1, Pop #1), "Finding It Out," "Grown Up Wrong," "If You Held the Key," "The Lisa Story." 10 from The Subtle Distinctions Love You More! Atco, 1973: "Painting of a Fool" (R&B #18). 11-13 from On His Own (BRJ solo), Atco, 1972, "As I Quietly Walk" (R&B #12, Pop # 48), "It Matters More", "This Eagle's Flown". 14-16 from Take It, Baby, (BRJ solo), Atco, 1973: "Careless" (R&B #24), "Lover of Women," "A Boy Is Crying." 17-18 BRJ solo single, Fantasy, 1975: "Who's Callin' Me?" (R&B #63), b/w "Crib Jam." /Track/ 19 BRJ guest appearance on Dufus Funkstrong's "(Did You Press Your) Bump Suit" (R&B #56, Pop #100), Casablanca, 1978. 20-21 unreleased BRJ demos, 1977-1979: "Smile Around Your Cigarette," "It's Raining Teeth."

In Praise of Underappreciated Books and Writers

WEBB PIERCE'S "THERE STANDS THE GLASS"

by Ken Tucker

It is a perfect song—not just a perfect *country* song—whose pleasure is only intensified by the way its impeccably controlled construction and performance courts imperfection: loss of control of one's life. Recorded and released in 1953, "There Stands the Glass" is the starkly sketched story of a man who walks into a bar and orders a drink, ponders its curative powers and its curse, and immediately falls into a reverie of regret and self-pity. After stating the title, the singer, Webb Pierce, avers that the glass's contents "will ease all my pain" and "will settle my brain," even as the quaver in his voice lets you know *he* knows he's deluding him-

self. He ends the first verse with an avowal suffused with a shame highly unusual for pre-recovery-era country music: "It's my first one today."

I've long thought that "There Stands the Glass" would make an ideal anthem for Alcoholics Anonymous, for the way it makes drinking sound so utterly dreary, and for the way "It's my first one today" contains an echo of the AA abstinence mantra "One day at a time." Instead, the song upon its release was interpreted as an unabashed hymn to getting shit-faced— was, indeed, banned by a number of country-music stations. Fred Rose, one of the most influential figures in country-music history as co-owner of the all-powerful Acuff-Rose Music Publishing company and by a number of accounts himself a reformed alcoholic, understood the allure of the song, and is said to have tried to dissuade Pierce from releasing it, protesting, "It hasn't even got a moral!" Instead, Pierce reveled in the song's success, referring to it as "the national anthem of barroom songs," one that quickly inspired a temperance answer-record called "Throw the Glass Away."

The bridge of "There Stands the Glass" occurs two verses in—when, in metaphoric time, the contents of the glass's first couple of gulps have warmed the singer's throat and soul and loosened his tongue. It's a four-line marvel of condensed mixed-emotionalism. It begins, "I'm wond'ring where you are tonight / I wonder if you are alright," the singer expressing concern for a lost love before moving onto the real purpose of his sodden lament—utter, unearned self-absorption: "I wonder if you think of me/ In my misery." No one who has ever listened closely to "There Stands the Glass" could possibly believe that the vocalist's long-gone honey is now thinking of him, or indeed gives two hoots about him. Instead, it's more likely that this fellow's line of palaver (ostensible concern for another person, immediately giving way to feeling sorry for himself) is one big reason the girl left him in the first place. Settling more seriously into his funk as a keening steel guitar—the signature honky-tonk instrument—wafts up and around his vocal, the narrator

resumes the previous metrical form and tells the bartender to fill his now-empty glass "up to the brim / Till my troubles grow dim." That last line would seem an unlikely occurrence any time soon: the only time this guy's troubles will dim is when he passes out later in his lonely hotel room, or, more likely, right there on the bar stool.

When he released "There Stands the Glass," Webb Pierce was twenty-six years old, a Louisiana-born former clothing salesman for Sears Roebuck with four #1 country hit singles under his belt. It's almost miraculous, really, that Pierce—who'd never specialized in fifties country music's perennial topics, drinking heavily and fornicating beyond the bounds of marriage—found it within himself to summon up the abject, insidious, grandly beautiful despair that suffuses his recording of "There Stands the Glass." Pierce, who died in 1991, had a soft, doughy face and brilliantined hair, a nice pair of jug ears, and a fondness for the garish suits designed by the Nashville custom clothier Nudie Cohen: a typical Nudie suit was lime green or pink or orange, appliquéd with swirling musical notes or flowery vines. After he became a star, Pierce drove a car whose steering wheel and interior were studded with silver dollars and had pistols as door handles; the singer installed a guitar-shaped swimming pool in his backyard. (In the seventies, long after he'd placed no fewer than fifty songs in the Top 10 of the country-music charts and the hits had stopped coming, he charged tourists to troop through his property and admire these artifacts.) Pierce was a dependable, upbeat guy, one who caught his biggest break in 1952, when he replaced his genre's greatest star, Hank Williams, on the all-important Nashville Saturday-night industry show-case and radio show, *The Grand Ole Opry,* at a point when Williams was doing real-life variations on filling glasses up to the brim—doing speed, missing tour and Opry dates.

Unlike Williams, a gaunt genius of ceaseless creativity, the pudgy Pierce wrote few of his own hits. The authorship of "There Stands the Glass" is cred-ited to Russ Hull, Mary Jean Shurtz, and Audrey Grisham, but was written only by Hull and Shurtz. Grisham was Pierce's wife; in a practice com-mon in that era, a popular artist could demand an additional profit by secur-ing a songwriting credit, either for himself (Pierce is listed as co-writer on any number of songs he did little more than agree to carry into the record-

ing studio) or, as in this case, a relative. And it was a relative of my own—my father—who inspired me to think about this song as much as I have. "There Stands the Glass" was one song among many that were playing the night my father, drunk, took a rifle out of our livingroom closet and held it to my mother's throat. "You want me to *use* this?" he yelled, his usually deep voice cracking into a shat-tered-glass scream on the word *use.* "You want me to use this?" he yelled again. "No, Doug," my mother said quietly. "Stop it. For Jesus's sake, go to bed."

When I asked my mother about this old scene recently, she said I had the music wrong. "Your father was listening

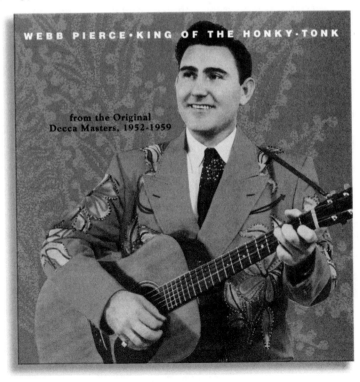

only to Willie Nelson by then," she said, as if she'd kept track of the progress of his alcoholism by the singers he favored—not a bad measure, when I thought about it later. After all, people do go on music jags as much as they do on booze-, movie-, or ice cream-jags, and my father did tend to obsess on favorites for defined periods. For a few years, George Jones was the best singer on earth. Then it was the syrupy country crooner Ray Price. Then Willie Nelson, with whose "outlaw" period my father nurtured a pathetic identification. Each shift in taste signaled a different phase of his obnoxiousness (as far as I and my siblings were concerned) or his sinning (as he would eventually, in thrall to AA and the church, more loftily consider it).

My mother and I had the Pierce vs. Nelson discussion shortly after my father died, a few years ago, when the inside of his own throat had closed over with cancer. I went down to Florida to go through his possessions with my brother and sister. When my sister asked my mother if she could have a particular Ray Price album, Mom said quickly, "Take it; it gives me the

She'd kept track of the progress of his alcoholism by the singers he favored — not a bad measure, when I thought about it later.

creeps. It has that song he used to play over and over again when he was with that woman"—and that was how I found out that, when I was a dull, self-absorbed teenager, my father had had an affair with the wife of one of his best friends; that my mother knew about it and did nothing to stop it; and that in her mind it had all played out to repeated playings of Price's maudlin hit "For the Good Times": my father dancing to the song with this other woman, both of them drunk, his huge hand damp against the back of her thin cotton dress.

But I remain convinced that there was a Webb Pierce greatest-hits collection in the pile of vinyl albums stacked on the record changer of the big living room stereo the night the rifle came out of the closet. Maybe, as my mother believes, "There Stands the Glass" wasn't playing at the exact moment the gunmetal found the pulse in her neck as swiftly as if its throb was a magnet. When my father's voice broke into the high-pitched yowl of "You want me to *use* this?," whatever song may have actually been on the turntable, it was the dolorous agony that pours forth from "There Stands the Glass" that filled up our living room like whiskey filled to a tumbler's rim, leaving the room—like that glass, like his throat—airless.

No More Bull: Sandy Bull and the Deep Song of the Sixties

by Bill Wadsworth

Pull my daisy
Tip my cup
All my eggs are broken.
Cut my thoughts for coconuts
All my doors are open.

—from "Pull My Daisy," by Jack Kerouac, Allen Ginsberg, and Neal Cassady, 1959

Before there was "world music" or "fusion," there was Sandy Bull.

In 1959, at the height of the folk-music revival, Bull was eighteen and already well on his way as a serious musician. Like many others at the time, his interest in music had been inspired by the Weavers, and he was fortunate enough to have learned guitar and banjo directly from Weavers' Mike Seeger and Erik Darling. But it was the less intimate influence of Pete Seeger that proved formative. The elder Weaver's internationalism cleared a path for Bull out of the backwoods and cotton fields of Americanist music into a different realm, a wider expanse of space, time, and musical modes.

That year Bull took off for a brief stint as a street musician in Paris: "We played under the bridges along the Seine, and people would shower francs on us. We went to a café, Ali's, in the Algerian section, and that was the first time I heard people playing oudlike instruments and style."

Open sesame.

In 1959, Ornette Coleman's historic ten-week stint at the Five Spot opened the door to a new freedom from musical convention in jazz, to the outrage of some and the exhilaration of others. It was a moment of crossover, of not looking back, of transition from subculture to counterculture. When the Coleman quartet returned for a second engagement in the spring of 1960, John Coltrane was there every night. It was a breakthrough of influence, a catalyst to Coltrane's genius that made possible the transcendent purity of "A Love Supreme" and "Meditations" a few years later.

Sandy Bull, back in the States after listening to Algerian music in Paris, was also in the Coleman's audience. But what he was drawn to most was not Coleman's saxophone or Don Cherry's trumpet, it was the drumming of Billy Higgins. At that moment an affinity was forged, and a lifelong friendship, that fused the two musicians' folk and jazz sensibilities. Together Bull and Higgins would, as Ezra Pound said, Make It New.

Open sesame.

Bull recorded his first album, *Fantasias for Banjo and Guitar*, for Vanguard in 1962, at the age of twenty-one. The centerpiece of the album is a twenty-two-minute improvisation entitled "Blend," featuring Bull on guitar and Higgins on drums. Since delving into African music and free jazz, Bull had been listening to Ali Akbar Khan's renditions of classical Indian ragas. The result is "Blend"—and it is on "Blend" that Bull's reputation as a musician's musician's musician is permanently secured. No one had ever heard anything like it before on guitar; it is the Ur-source for the psychedelic raga rock of the mid- and late sixties, as well as arguably the proliferation of all kinds of nontraditional open-tuned guitar work that drove sixties music.

Bull was immediately established as the ultimate eclecticist, whose albums combined a wild assortment of genres and traditions, from Chuck Berry to Bach, from fourteenth-century ballades to salsa and samba to Indian, African, and Middle Eastern music. His instruments eventually included oud, sarod, six-string bass, pedal steel, and drums as well as guitar and banjo. But the core of Bull's genius wasn't versatility, virtuosity, or even his eclecticism; it was his rage to synthesize. Bach on banjo, bossa nova on oud, and especially raga on guitar: It was imaginative transgressions such as these, with their intermixing in works like "Blend," that made him a true original and a seminal influence on far more famous musicians who followed, among them Jimi Hendrix, Steve Winwood, Patti Smith and Bob Dylan. His style was a precursor to those of Leo Kottke, John Fahey, and Ralph Towner; his groundbreaking use of open tunings foreshadowed Joni Mitchell, Stephen Stills, and the power chords of Keith Richards.

According to legend, it was Sandy Bull, during a stay in Woodstock in the summer of 1964, who persuaded Dylan to commit his own act of transgression by picking up an electric guitar. A year later, at Newport, when Dylan performed with the Band to a chorus of boos, the folk revival was eclipsed for good by rock.

Open sesame.

In 1963, Bull befriended Hamza El Din, the Nubian oud master, whom he met on the Via Veneto in Rome, and with whom he later shared apartments in New York and San Francisco. El Din's first album, released by Vanguard in the mid-sixties, was one of the first "world music" recordings to receive widespread recognition in the West. In 1964, Bull recorded his second album, *Inventions*, which features "Blend 2." "Blend 2" is more complicated and adventurous than "Blend," and this time the presiding spirit is more Hamza El Din than Ali Akbar Khan. The description of "Blend 2" by Nat Hentoff in the liner notes is worth quoting:

> The rhythmically ad-lib opening mood is surfacely tranquil but restless beneath. The first recognizable tune is a sketch of "Lonely Woman" by Ornette Coleman. After fragments of an Ali Akbar Khan melody, there is a brief paraphrase of "Pretty Polly," followed by a change of key to the dominant. (It is here the

tempo doubles, and in this dominant section can be found influences of Lebanese music, plus several choruses of a North African popular song.) Billy Higgins emerges in a fascinatingly constructed drum solo of both continuity and sensitivity. "Blend 2" keeps rising with a Cairo theme, actually an identifying motif from the Egyptian singer Om Koulsom's recording, "Ya Zalemni."

Without a break or a sense of gratuitous superimposition, Bull moves to "Wabash Cannonball"; a tune from Pakistan (heard on a jukebox at a Pakistani restaurant in New York); a simplified Afghanistan-style tune; a paraphrase of "The Young Man Who Couldn't Hoe Corn". . . and finally, in swiftly accelerating tempo, an exploration of the tonalities of what has gone before as well as a stretching out of rhythmic possibilities. (This turbulent conclusion is based on a practice heard at the end of some Indian ragas, though not on any one particular raga.)

After 1964, Bull was taken down by a heroin habit. He didn't return to the style and tuning of "Blend" and "Blend 2" for twenty years, and by that time he was all but forgotten as a musician. His performances became notorious nonperformances, incoherent, stumbling, and solipsistic. Patti Smith wrote, "It was the strangest thing I ever saw. His sense of space and time was slightly science fiction. A leftover junk space." In 1968, an outraged Grover Sales wrote a devastating piece entitled "Goodbye Sandy Bull" and soon rumors began to circulate that Bull had died. Patti Smith again: "Some said he was dead, car crash. 3 notches under James Dean. Some say his end was more decadent. More Paris in the twenties. Slain in some alley. A fizzled goofball brain." Ben Fong-Torres wrote a piece on Bull in *Rolling Stone* in 1970 entitled "Hey, I Thought You Were Dead."

Sandy Bull was not dead. He kicked his habit in 1974 and made a comeback of sorts playing oud in Dylan's Rolling Thunder Revue in 1975. But after recording his last album for Vanguard, aptly called *Demolition Derby*, in 1972, he didn't release another recording for sixteen years. He remained a restless and innovative outsider on the music scene, eventually moving closer to his Americanist roots and settling outside Nashville in the early nineties. But his early recordings went out of print and his later ones were largely ignored. The impact of those first two albums, which he recorded between the ages of twenty-one and twenty-three, would never be repeated, and scarcely remembered.

In certain pieces of music—Coltrane's "A Love Supreme" or Sandy Bull's "Blend"—one hears a common open-endedness, a timelessness, a bottomless quality that seems to me to strike the radical chord of a time when for a historical moment "all the doors were open." Technically, on the guitar, this may be explained by the phenomenon of open tuning and the use of drone notes. Through open tuning, Bull was able to reach forward to a new openness in musical consciousness and simultaneously to reach back to musics and modes of consciousness far more ancient than ours. García Lorca, tracing the same quality in Gypsy music back to similar roots in India, called it *cante jondo*—"deep song." What he said of deep song may be the best description I know of the supreme instrumental meditations of Coltrane and Bull:

> Notice, gentlemen, the transcendence of deep song, and how rightly our people call it "deep." It is truly deep, deeper than all the wells and seas that surround the world, much deeper than the present heart that creates it or the voice that sings it, because it is almost infinite. It comes from remote races and crosses the graveyard of the years and the fronds of parched winds. It comes from the first sob and the first kiss.

Open sesame.

I called Sandy Bull to interview him for this piece, only to learn from his wife, Candy Bull, that he had died four months earlier, on April 11, 2001, at the

Sandy Bull was not dead. He kicked his habit in 1974 and made a comeback of sorts playing oud in Dylan's Rolling Thunder Revue in 1975.

age of sixty. He left two sons, Jesse and Jackson, and a daughter, K.C., who in recent years had been performing with him. I learned he had a brother named Digger St. John and that his sister was Daisy Paradis, the well-known American sitar player. His stepfather was Geoffrey Hellman, a staff writer for the *New Yorker*, and his first mentor, it turned out, was his mother, who was an accomplished classical harpist. It sounded like a good life, and his career had lately been reviving, thanks in part to the long-delayed rerelease in the late nineties of his early Vanguard recordings.

Billy Higgins died three weeks after Sandy Bull.

Close sesame.

SISYPHUS RISING
by Nuar Alsadir

In his beginning was his end. *Five Leaves Left*, twenty-one-year-old Nick Drake's 1969 debut album, brought a new musical voice to the world and at the same time cast a shadow over it. The title, taken from the warning label found near the end of a pack of Rizla cigarette papers, suggested that he had only so much time to burn. Five years later, Drake was dead from an overdose of antidepressants, a copy of Camus's *The Myth of Sisyphus* laying on his bedside table. His mother, who found him there, thought the book's presence "might have been trying to tell me something."

The Myth of Sisyphus, though it describes severe anguish, calls for the sufferer to persevere and create even in the midst of pain. The question within this call—whether or not life is worth living—is the one Drake faced in his final years. Like Sisyphus, whose "whole being," according to Camus, "is exerted toward accomplishing nothing," Drake put all of his energy into albums that never reached a broad public during his lifetime. Intensely shy, and unwilling or unable to play in front of an audience, he nevertheless craved the attention that other singer-songwriters (such as fellow Island Records recording artist Cat Stevens) were receiving at the time.

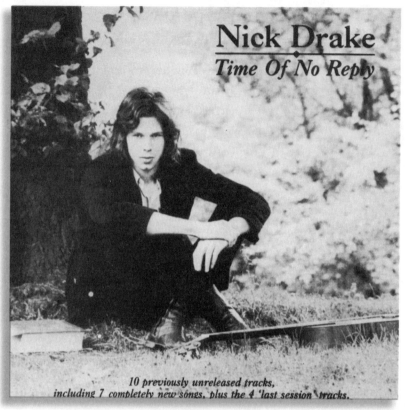

10 previously unreleased tracks,
including 7 completely new songs, plus the 4 'last session tracks.

Drake was, by all accounts, a person who had difficulty carrying on even the most basic conversation and who expressed himself primarily through song—making his desire for listeners all the more acute. He poured his intimacy into music at the expense of life. As he put it in "Hazey Jane II," "If songs were lines in a conversation / the situation would be fine."

Where it wasn't fine in life, it was in music. His best work is minimalist and symbolic, belonging outside the time of ordinary conversation, and culminates in his third album, *Pink Moon*. Drake, having already turned inward, insisted that the music be stripped down, and recorded the entire album in just two nights. Gone were the lush arrangements and the background vocals. Gone were his collaborations with other artists. Even his record company had been left out: the advertisement for *Pink Moon* insisted that the executives at Island Records weren't even aware of the album until it was finished. What remained was

Although *Five Leaves Left* sold modestly well for a debut from an unknown songwriter and left him hopeful, Drake was devastated when his second album, *Bryter Layter*—which took nine months to record and was overproduced in an effort to make it more marketable—did not fare much better.

Some attribute the onset of Drake's depression to this insufficient response to his music, and his nihilistic outlook to having twice pushed the great boulder of creativity up the hill only to watch it roll down again. It's hard to know for sure, as the songwriter alone with himself, in dialogue with his mind.

This moment of interiority is one Camus describes at the end of Sisyphus's long struggle, the pause as he watches the rock roll back down the hill but before he meets it at the bottom to start over again. "It is during that return, that pause," writes Camus, "that Sisyphus interests me," because "that hour, like a breathing-space which returns as surely as his suffering . . . is the hour of consciousness."

It is also the hour of song. Listening to *Pink Moon* we feel not only close to Drake, but opened by him. Even though it is he who sings, it is us he confesses. Nearly all of his music—characterized by a spellbinding dissonance of cluster chords and an ethereal, haunted voice hovering over a small range—possesses this illuminating, mythic quality, but it is with *Pink Moon* that he is truly in his hour. There is a stark, late-night intimacy to the songs. Everyone has gone to sleep. You and Drake are alone in a small, dark room, autumn's first chill is blowing in, and you're on the brink of some enormous emotion you've never felt before. This music contains the best aspects of being awake—it holds you in your own hour of consciousness.

For Drake, this consciousness could sometimes be chilling. In the last year of his life, he recorded four songs, released posthumously on *Time of No Reply*. By then he was in such bad shape that he couldn't sing and play guitar at the same time: the engineer recorded the guitar parts separately and overdubbed the vocals. These four last songs are spare and circular and rely on emotionally laden symbols more than verbal expression. In "Black Eyed Dog," the repetition of notes and lines hammers out the barren desperation of his plea. "Black dog," once a term for the devil, was, by the time Drake wrote his song, a fairly common euphemism for depression. The strain in Drake's voice gives the sense that he is fixed on the dog's eyes even as he sings.

"If this myth is tragic," writes Camus, "that is because its hero is conscious." As Camus explains of Oedipus, "at the outset [he] obeys fate without knowing it. But from the moment he knows, his tragedy begins." Nonetheless, the same mind that recognizes torment as tragedy also finds, within that anguish, joy. Like *The Myth of Sisyphus*, *Pink Moon* closes on a hopeful note, summoning us to "rise" and "go play the game you learned from the morning." In the midst of our own suffering, we can learn from the mourning and find freedom in consciousness. Drake's music thus awakens the most valuable part of ourselves, "For everything," Camus reminds us, "begins with consciousness and nothing is worth anything except through it."

BOB DYLAN'S TARANTULA

by Edward Hill

Bob Dylan is the author of some five hundred songs and poems. Some, like "Blowin' in the Wind," "The Times They Are A-Changin'," and, "Like A Rollin' Stone," are generational anthems that inalterably transformed and elevated the character of American popular song.

Tarantula, Dylan's single published book, is rarely mentioned.

The fault is not the publisher's. According to the unnamed author of the foreword to *Tarantula*, a pleasingly slim tome released by Macmillan in 1971, they "weren't quite sure what to make of the book except money." And they certainly tried. Before *Tarantula*'s original intended release in 1966, Macmillan printed shopping bags and lapel buttons sporting Dylan's photograph over the title (see: eBay). Precisely the kind of marketing one might expect our generation's most exalted bard to find offensive. But one remembers that the bard had previously declined an invitation from Lawrence Ferlinghetti to join his stable of espresso-swilling poets at City Lights in San Francisco. It would be bright lights in the big city for Dylan.

Or would it be more in the nature of a practical joke against the house that brought the world Yeats by the mystical rabbi whom Don McLean called "the jester"? In *Positively Fourth Street*, David Hadju describes the hilarious scene in David Markel's office at Macmillan when Dylan and Joan Baez came by after hours to discuss terms. Hadju's account of the fifteen-minute meeting portrays the 1965 "Establishment" bewilderment with the startling new cultural phenomenon called "rock star." Hadju also shows how stars like Dylan and Baez could exploit that bewilderment. Dylan received a ten-thousand-dollar advance for approximately two hundred pages of "episodic . . . prose poetry pieces" due in one year. Nice work if you can get it. Better work if you don't actually do it. Dylan didn't. Like most of Dylan's professional and artistic pursuits, *Tarantula* was shelved as a result of the Great Woodstock Country-Road Motorsickle Smash-Up of July 29, 1966. Hence the publication in 1971, a date determined, we are informed in the foreword, by the fact that "Bob wants it published, and so now is the time to publish it."

Publish what? "Episodic . . . prose poetry pieces" to be sure, but *Tarantula* is certainly neither a novel nor poetry. Not even epic poetry. Dylan is a famously reticent and opaque character. He is clearly a genius, and a compelling one for his reticence. Loving Dylan can be like having sex with a fabulously beautiful and sensuous woman who doesn't speak one's language. One's desire to "know" the other can become obsessive, even delusory. She

Tarantula is neither coherent nor "about" anything. It presents a kaleidoscopic effusion of images, lyrics, attitudes, emotions, and rhythms that leave the reader saying, "So that is what was on his mind."

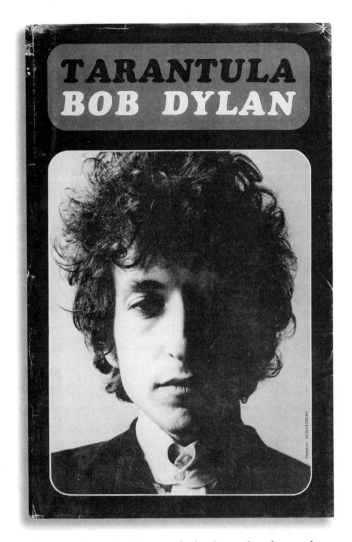

speaks of the weather and one hears Blake. Dylan writes "episodic . . . prose poetry pieces" and one is suddenly blessed with vision into the mind of "our" genius. Or so one feverishly wishes. And, remarkably, the wish is sometimes fulfilled.

Tarantula is neither coherent nor "about" anything. It presents a kaleidoscopic effusion of images, lyrics, attitudes, emotions, and rhythms that leave the reader saying, "So that is what was on his mind." Of Dylan's other writings in common circulation, the closest example of *Tarantula*'s predominant style is the first of the three untitled stanzas on the back cover of *Bringing It All Back Home,* released in March 1965. The writing is rife with pop-culture and musicological references, suggestions of poetic meter, a recurrent cynicism regarding the politics of the day, and unbridled surrealism. Categorically, the style is Beat. Historically, *Tarantula* is an unparalleled catalog of Dylan's brainstorming, influences, and rages during the years in which he composed and recorded *Another Side of Bob Dylan, Bringing It All Back Home, Highway 61 Revisited,* and, *Blonde on Blonde* and, in so doing, became one of the most significant and influential artists of this century. In the midst of the literary hallucination that is *Tarantula*, the reader is tempted repeatedly to shout, "Now I get him! It's all here!" Maybe so. Or maybe, drenched in postcoital sweat, the reader's other-languaged lover is looking deep into his eyes asking for bus fare as the reader imagines song.

Dylan never gave it away. In a famously evasive interview with Jack Goddard of the *Village Voice* published on March 25, 1965, Dylan described his work in progress as "a funny book" about "angels." Okay. Robert Shelton described it as "an enigma wrapped in a question mark." What is left to say?

Perhaps it is best to follow Dylan's lead. In 1966, *Playboy* magazine asked him what his songs were about. Dylan responded, "Oh, some are about four minutes; some are about five; and, some, believe it or not, are about eleven or twelve." *Tarantula* is about 140 pages.

JAZZ HEAVEN: ART BLAKEY'S JAZZ MESSENGERS!!!
by Richard Edson

In the late sixties, as a tender but opinionated young teenager and aspiring musician, I opened my ears to the music called jazz. In the late sixties everything, including jazz, seemed to be falling apart.

If you weren't dying in Vietnam or getting shot at in Mississippi it was an exciting time to be young. And an exciting time to be getting into jazz. Jazz intrigued me, but it also intimidated me because I really didn't get it. There was bebop, hard bop, swing, free jazz, West Coast, post-bop, cool, soul jazz, Latin jazz, Brazilian jazz, and Miles Davis's electronic explorations. Disputes raged in obscure journals about the proper direction of jazz, and angry black nationalists claimed Afro-American sanctity for the music. But for a white kid stuck in suburbia and unable to make a connection to the rock and roll drug subculture, jazz offered a cool way out. Or a cool way in, as the case may be.

Once or twice a month, or whenever we could get one of our mothers to drive us, a couple of young music snobs and I would descend on Sam Goody's at the Cross County Shopping Center in Yonkers, New York, to buy one jazz record apiece for $2.89 or $3.89.

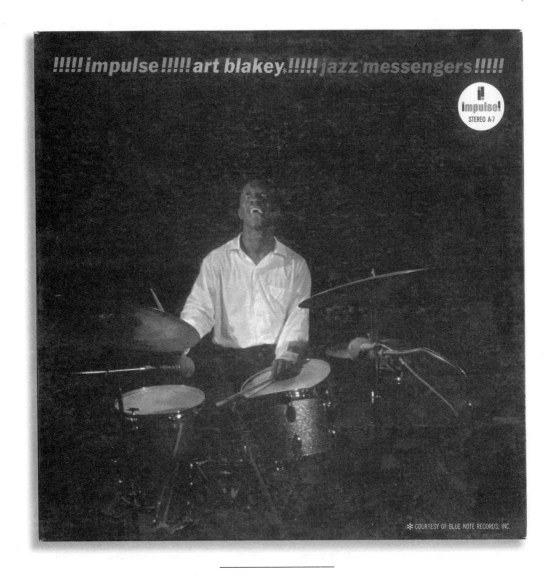

!!!!!impulse!!!!!art blakey∗!!!!!jazz messengers!!!!!

impulse!
STEREO A-7

∗ COURTESY OF BLUE NOTE RECORDS, INC.

For a white kid stuck in suburbia and unable to make a connection to the rock and roll drug subculture, jazz offered a cool way out. Or a cool way in, as the case may be.

It was in the course of one of these outings that I chanced upon *Art Blakey!!! Jazz Messengers!!!* on Impulse Records. It was the jacket that sold me (the most common motivation behind my purchasing decisions). Art Blakey was portrayed playing a drum kit, his eyes gazing heavenward, an ecstatic smile on his face. He was lit by moody red and white lights and surrounded by a deep, velvety blackness. The title was in small orange, yellow, and purple print, and the red, black, and white Impulse logo was in the corner. It also had the distinctive orange-and-black spine that was an Impulse trademark.

A couple of years later, while still in high school, I visited my older sister in Boston. She was attending an all-girls college there, so I had to stay with her new boyfriend at Harvard University. Even though they were only a few years older, I was intimidated to be keeping such brainy, sophisticated company. I noticed his roommate's record collection on a small shelf above a little portable stereo system. Half of the records had the telltale orange-and-black spines of Impulse. The idea that someone had so many records from the coolest record company in the world was just too much for me. I couldn't even speak to the guy.

But back to Art Blakey's *Jazz Messengers*. When I listened to it on my family's Scott stereo system I was instantly caught up in its lilting, three-horn funkiness. It was melodic and driving, emotional and smart. I rejoiced at my new purchase and praised my ability to pick 'em.

I was low key when I told my friends about it. It was "all right," I told them, "but come over and judge for yourselves." They did, and we sat there in my parents' living room nodding our heads and tapping our toes and smiling our secret hypercool suburban jazz smiles, signifying that we had all just died and gone to jazz heaven.

Jazz Messengers!!! is one of Art Blakey's great but seldom heard and, until recently, hardest-to-find albums. Blakey, who, with his quartet, quintet, and Jazz Messengers, provided a training ground and graduate school for some of the greatest soloists and bandleaders of two or three generations, including Horace Silver, Donald Byrd, Hank Mobley, Wynton and Branford Marsalis, Freddie Hubbard, Bobby Timmons, and Jackie McLean. This one featured an unparalleled front line including the great Lee Morgan on trumpet, the genius Wayne Shorter on tenor sax, and the underrated but always soulful Curtis Fuller on trombone. Each song is a gem, ranging from hard-bop funkiness to Latin-tinged swing to romantic, sensitive ballads. My favorite is "Alamode," the opener on side one, written by Curtis Fuller.

Part of the ritual, and fun, of buying jazz records was obsessing over the jackets' art, photography, and liner notes. Most of the jazz records of the fifties and sixties had extensive liner notes, written by the leading jazz "authorities" of the day. They gave an intellectual and historical charge to the simple act of listening to music, and as a budding jazz musician I would slavishly read and reread them, hoping to glean the knowledge that I suspected lay within this foreign but very American world of jazz.

Of course, looking back, I realize jazz was, for the budding musician, probably the most difficult and least remunerative of musical styles and, for a white guy, the one musical style most fraught with racial land mines. There was also the jazz musician's inherent snobbery, one-upmanship, and extreme celebration of musical virtuosity. Rock, by contrast, seemed so simple and accessible that any idiot could play it. Which, in my snobby mind, was exactly who I thought was playing it. Idiots. Which was why I turned my back on it. That is, until 1976, when the Ramones and the Sex Pistols shook the musical world. After years of struggling with chords and their countless inversions, the scales and scale patterns, not to mention the songs, that constituted the jazz canon, and its crowning glory, improvisation, it was a relief to give up playing the trumpet and

Rock, by contrast, seemed so simple.

start playing drums and play them loud, angry, and simple. What a relief. What freedom.

So rock, in the form of punk, saved my musical soul—not because I played punk, but because it blew open the doors of what music could and should be and who could and should play it. Bebop jazz and beyond was, and is, an elitist musical form, played by and for people who strangle on its own arcane strictures.

Jazz was dead.

Long live jazz.

For jazz, the good stuff, the real stuff, really is about a feeling, a rhythm, a respect for tradition while remaining completely open to anything and everything that can be incorporated into it (which is just about everything). Since punk rock scorched the musical landscape and blew the door off the barn, everything has been allowed. Style, now, is purely a matter of taste. But the feeling of jazz, its freedom and roots in improvisation and the social dance, seems like the perfect path back into music for me.

So once again I return to Art Blakey's *Jazz Messengers!!!* on Impulse Records. The cover is a little worn and the record is a little scratched, but the sound is still fine, like old wine, and the music within still transports me to jazz—no, not jazz—to musical heaven. ▪

NOT THE LITTLE BOY

Innocence and Experience in the Music of Brian Wilson

BY ANDREW HULTKRANS

S"Hello, Mr. Wilson . . ."

ometime in the spring of 1967, Brian Wilson, the pop wunderkind behind the music of the Beach Boys, heard these words as he wandered into a screening of the John Frankenheimer film *Seconds*. He was, at the time, sporadically working on what was to become the most legendary unreleased album in rock history, originally titled *Dumb Angel* but later called *Smile*, and he was losing his mind. According to a friend who was at Wilson's house when he returned from the movie theater, *Seconds* had a profound effect on the young composer.

I ONCE KNEW

Agitated, Wilson related how the first thing he heard was someone saying hello to him. "It completely blew my mind," he said. Then: "That's not all . . . the whole thing was there. I mean my whole life. Birth and death and rebirth. Even the beach was in it. It was my whole life right there on the screen." When his friend suggested it might be a coincidence, Wilson replied, "What if it's real? You know there's mind gangsters these days. There could be mind gangsters, couldn't there? I mean look at [Phil] Spector, he could be involved in it, couldn't he? He's going into films. How hard would it be for him to set something up like that?" Convinced to calm down, Wilson picked up a pen and a piece of paper and drew a growth curve as he began to talk about music: "Spector started the whole thing. He

was the first one to use the studio. But I've gone beyond him now. I'm doing the spiritual sound, a white spiritual sound. Religious music. Did you hear the Beatles album [*Revolver*]? Religious, right? That's the whole movement. That's where I'm going. . . . It's going to scare a lot of people when I get there."

In the previous year, Wilson had reached two artistic peaks: he had written, arranged, and produced *Pet Sounds*, an album that introduced new levels of orchestration and harmonic sophistication to rock music, and had followed it with the single "Good Vibrations," a multi-movement "pocket symphony" that employed modular recording (fragments of the song were recorded over five months at several studios), experimental editing, and the unearthly howl of a

theremin. In between sessions for "Good Vibrations," Wilson began work on *Smile*, a spiritual song cycle that would evoke the innocence of youth—a "teenage symphony to God." To counter the Beatles, and the British bands and fashions that ruled these shores in 1966, Wilson wanted the music to be distinctly American, but not in the way that "Surfin' U.S.A." and "California Girls" were American. Concerned about the country's lost innocence in the wake of the JFK assassination and the rapidly escalating Vietnam conflict, Wilson sought to recapture the optimism and homespun simplicity (one of the tracks would be called "Cabinessence") of nineteenth-century Americana. To this end, he began to collaborate with a similarly prodigious talent, Van Dyke Parks, whose "American Gothic trip," a Randy Newman-esque fascination with early American music, the Deep South, and the pioneer West, jibed with his intentions for the album. With Parks as his lyricist and sounding board, Wilson set about writing and recording *Smile* in May 1966.

He also came seriously unhinged. Over the following months, he would build a custom sandbox in his dining room to house his grand piano; replace all his living room furniture with gym mats and exercise equipment (which he then never used); buy boxloads of identical children's dolls (which he then never opened); hold

Al Jardine, the squarest Beach Boy, captive in his car as he drove around the William Morris parking lot twenty times, raving about an LSD trip he had just taken; insist that his studio musicians wear firemen's helmets for the duration of a recording session; scrap the resulting "Fire"

OVER THE FOLLOWING MONTHS, HE WOULD INSIST THAT HIS STUDIO MUSICIANS WEAR FIREMEN'S HELMETS FOR THE DURATION OF A RECORDING SESSION.

music because he believed it had caused a rash of fires around L.A.; banish an acquaintance's girlfriend from the studio because he thought she was a witch who was "messing with his brain" by means of ESP; and, as ever, worry about Phil Spector, playing "Be My Baby" over and over again, as if *dum-da-dum-cha* signaled the beginning of a mystical Morse code that would transmit the secret of the universe.

Paranoia about "mind gangsters" aside, it isn't difficult to see why *Seconds* got under Wilson's skin. A dark, mildly psychedelic film reminiscent of *The Twilight Zone*, *Seconds* is the tale of Arthur Hamilton, an unbearably bland, world-weary middle-aged banker—the ultimate "man in the gray flannel suit"—who is lured by an old friend into literally signing his life away to a shadowy company that offers "rebirth" services. In exchange for thirty thousand dollars, the company stages a death, provides a plausible corpse, and awards the remaining family a handsome insurance settlement. The client then receives exten-

sive plastic surgery, a manufactured personal history, a dream career (based on subconscious wishes teased out through Pentothal and regression therapy), and a well-appointed home in a ritzy community. (Emphasizing just how extensive the plastic surgery really is, the surgeon—played by the actor who would later portray Oscar Goldman in *The Six Million Dollar Man*—says, in an insinuating tone, "*Everything* is different.") Through this procedure, Hamilton is transformed into an inconspicuously successful artist named Tony Wilson, played by Rock Hudson, and set up in a swank Malibu beach house, complete with personal assistant.

> He was a quiet man. It was as if he was always listening to something inside, some voice. . . . He fought so hard for what he'd been taught to want, and when he got it he just grew more and more confused.
>
> —Arthur Hamilton's wife, recalling her "late" husband, in *Seconds*

Though hardly the work of Phil Spector, the film's parallels to Wilson's life are eerie (beginning with the casting of Hudson, known for his romantic comedies with Doris Day, mother of Wilson's old friend and fellow surf-music producer Terry Melcher). Wilson was raised in what could be seen as an anthropological experiment in conservative, middle-class, 1950s suburbia: Hawthorne, California, a town

a one-man hit factory, churning out Top Ten singles by the month and leading the Beach Boys on grueling, sold-out concert tours. "A people pleaser," as his mother would later call him, the sensitive, introspective Wilson worked increasingly hard to become *the* consummate pop craftsman, driven by the need to placate his abusive, tyrannical father (a failed songwriter), his family (the Beach Boys consisted of his two brothers, his cousin, and a childhood friend), and the executives in "the Tower" (Capitol Records' iconic building). Along the way, like Hamilton, he lost track of himself.

It will be a transition from this present work. You see, you don't have to prove anything anymore. You are accepted. You will be in your own new dimension . . . absolved of all responsibility except to your own interests.

—"Rebirth" company psychiatrist, describing Arthur Hamilton's new life as artist Tony Wilson, in *Seconds*

BEFORE THE RELEASE OF PET SOUNDS, WILSON AND THE BEACH BOYS, WHILE SPECTACULARLY SUCCESSFUL, WERE REGARDED BY THE HIP COGNOSCENTI AS IMPOSSIBLY SQUARE.

not unlike the cheery SoCal burg depicted in *Invasion of the Body Snatchers* (an obvious influence on *Seconds*)—a town that would reproduce Arthur Hamiltons by the truckload. And, in certain circles, Wilson *was* an Arthur Hamilton. Before the release of *Pet Sounds*, Wilson and the Beach Boys, while spectacularly successful, were regarded by the hip cognoscenti as impossibly square—the fresh-faced, All-American sons of suburban salarymen, the very antithesis of urban bohemians. During this time, from 1962 to 1965, Wilson had been

The parallels do not end there: In *Seconds*, Rock Hudson suffers an anxiety attack on an airplane (after a stewardess says, "Hello, Mr. Wilson") on his way from Malibu to visit his old family house,

ONLY $~~59.80~~ $29.90

SUBSCRIBE & SAVE!

Enter my Charter Subscription to *Tin House* at the incredibly low Charter Rate of just $29.90 for one full year (four issues). I save 50% off the newsstand price!

NAME _____ (PLEASE PRINT)

ADDRESS _____

_____

CITY / STATE / ZIP

☐ **Payment Enclosed**

☐ **Please Bill Me**

For Canada add $15.00. All other foreign add $30.00 and send prepaid in U.S. funds. Please allow 6–8 weeks for delivery of your first issue.

MONEY-BACK SATISFACTION GUARANTEE

If you are ever less than completely satisfied with *Tin House* you may cancel your subscription and receive a refund for all unmailed issues — *No Questions Asked!*

B0010A

ONLY $~~59.80~~ $29.90

GIVE A GIFT & SAVE!

I want to give a gift subscription to *Tin House* at the incredibly low Charter Rate of just $29.90 for one full year (four issues). I save 50% off the newsstand price!

MY NAME _____ (PLEASE PRINT)

ADDRESS _____

CITY / STATE / ZIP

GIFT SUBSCRIPTION FOR _____ (PLEASE PRINT)

ADDRESS _____

CITY / STATE / ZIP

B0010B

☐ **Payment Enclosed**   ☐ **Please Bill Me**

For Canada add $15.00. All other foreign add $30.00 and send prepaid in U.S. funds. Please allow 6–8 weeks for delivery of first issue.

BUSINESS REPLY MAIL

FIRST-CLASS MAIL   PERMIT NO. 99027   ESCONDIDO CA

POSTAGE WILL BE PAID BY ADDRESSEE

NO POSTAGE
NECESSARY
IF MAILED
IN THE
UNITED STATES

TIN HOUSE
MAGAZINE
PO BOX 469049
ESCONDIDO CA 92046-9049

BUSINESS REPLY MAIL

FIRST-CLASS MAIL   PERMIT NO. 99027   ESCONDIDO CA

POSTAGE WILL BE PAID BY ADDRESSEE

NO POSTAGE
NECESSARY
IF MAILED
IN THE
UNITED STATES

TIN HOUSE
MAGAZINE
PO BOX 469049
ESCONDIDO CA 92046-9049

where, posing as a friend of Arthur Hamilton, he will speak to his former wife in order to recover some semblance of his lost self. After reminiscing about his previous incarnation with his "widow" (who now looks old enough to be his mother), Hudson resolves to return to the company and make a fresh start in a new identity. In December 1964, on a flight at the beginning of a Beach Boys tour, Brian Wilson had a nervous breakdown. The next day he flew back to Los Angeles, asking that his mother pick him up at the airport. When he arrived he demanded to be taken back to his childhood home in Hawthorne, which was empty but had not yet been sold. There, he had a soul-searching talk with his mother, during which he decided to stop touring with the Beach Boys so he could stay home and focus on writing and production.

Earlier in the film, Hudson is taken by his new (company-hired) girlfriend to a Dionysian festival, at which naked neo-pagan hippies cavort in a massive vat of grapes. At first, the conservative, out-of-place Hudson resists his girlfriend's pleas to join her in the vat. Eventually stripped and thrown in by the other revelers, Hudson finally relaxes, starts drinking, and begins to enjoy himself—he is baptized in his new identity. Relieved of his concert duties in 1965, Wilson immersed himself in creating increasingly sophisticated music for the Beach Boys; not coinciden-

tally, he was also being indoctrinated into L.A.'s burgeoning counterculture through various new hip friends and hangers-on. Against the protests of his wife, Wilson was encouraged by his bohemian friends to try pot, speed, and acid. Given LSD by a friend, Wilson "saw God" in a profound, life-altering experience that he would later say "tore his head off." Despite John Lennon's assurances about LSD on *Revolver* ("It is not dying"), Wilson was more than likely referring to his first acid trip—signifying his transformation from square to hip, from innocence to experience—when he claimed he saw his "death and rebirth" reflected in *Seconds*.

> Dionysian stirrings arise either through the influence of those narcotic potions of which all primitive races speak in their hymns, or through the powerful approach of spring, which penetrates with joy the whole frame of nature. So stirred, the individual forgets himself completely. . . . His Apollonian consciousness was but a thin veil hiding from him the whole Dionysian realm.
>
> —Friedrich Nietzsche, *The Birth of Tragedy*

Nietzsche would have hated *Pet Sounds*. He would have regarded it as the ne plus ultra of overwrought Apollonian schmaltz. In *The Birth of Tragedy*, he outlines two conflicting drives in ancient

Greek culture: the Apollonian, which promotes rational order, moral rectitude, naive optimism, and the individual will of man, and the Dionysian, which advocates the derangement of the senses, amorality, existential nihilism, and the instinctual will of nature. Nietzsche derived his concept of the Dionysian from Schopenhauer's view that irrational forces reside at the foundation of all creativity and of reality itself, and his concept of the Apollonian from Schopenhauer's *Principium individuationis* (individual principle), what we would loosely call the ego, which allows man to distinguish himself from others and protects him from the disordered nature of reality. Nietzsche lamented the suppression of the Dionysian in European culture since Socrates, and he would have pointed to the Beach Boys as evidence of a new, appallingly cheery American strain of the Apollonian—all surf, sun, and fun, fun, fun: ancient Greece repackaged as Waikiki—taking special note of Wilson's mastery as an arranger by the time of *Pet Sounds*, his ability to teach session musicians and the Beach Boys the complex parts he had previously worked out "in his head," and his perfectionist production style. (Although Mike Love is generally an unreliable commentator on the history of the Beach Boys, he was not altogether incorrect when he called *Pet Sounds* "Brian's ego music.") Tellingly, one *Pet Sounds* track, "I Know There's an Answer" (itself an Apollonian sentiment), was originally called "Hang On to Your Ego." In it, Wilson admonishes those who "isolate their heads and stay in their safety zones" with the chiding chorus, "Hang on to your ego / Hang on, but I know that you're gonna lose the fight." He might as well have been addressing himself.

If Nietzsche had been alive to write an updated, 1967 edition of *The Birth of Tragedy*, he would have been much encouraged, as he was in 1872 by the Dionysian stirrings he heard in Wagner, by the music of the Doors. Indeed, the entire history of late-sixties L.A. pop could be read as a shift from the sunny, healing Apollonian symphonies of Brian Wilson to the dark, disorienting, Dionysian cabaret of Jim Morrison. The Doors released their debut in January 1967, and it was during that winter that *Smile*, and Wilson himself, started to unravel. As winter gave way to spring, Wilson was dropping acid, recording discrete modules of the *Smile* tracks as he had for "Good Vibrations" (intending to "order" them later), and, through the L.A. hipoisie who had gathered around him to watch his next masterwork unfold, becoming aware of a Dionysian youth movement swelling under his feet. His work became more erratic, his collaborator Van Dyke Parks left and returned and left again, and, one by one, his other hip friends abandoned him, alienated by his increasingly paranoid behavior and sensing impending disaster. In early June, right before the Monterey Pop Festival, at which the Beach Boys were scheduled to play and which, appropriately, featured an image of Pan on its promotional fliers, Wilson inexplicably scrapped the *Smile* project, returning to the studio with the Beach Boys, rather than session musicians, to rerecord tracks for *Smile*'s anemic twin, *Smiley Smile*.

Over the years, many reasons have been floated to explain Wilson's inability to finish *Smile* and his subsequent withdrawal from public life in the seventies: drugs; mental illness; artistic self-consciousness; conflicts with Mike Love and the other Beach Boys; the Boys' 1967 royalty lawsuit against Capitol Records; the band's no-show at the Monterey Pop Festival; the overnight shift in countercultural tastes, at that very festival, from L.A.'s manufactured pop to San Francisco's "organic," improvisatory psychedelia; the release of *Sgt. Pepper's Lonely Hearts Club Band*; Jimi Hendrix's pronouncement on *Are You Experienced?* that "You'll never hear surf music again"; even, according to a critic for *Art Issues*, "the psychic fallout D. H. Lawrence finds in the great novels of Hawthorne and Melville," in which "indigenous New World demons exact a

deadening poetic justice upon any American cultural effort that seeks to combine the 'spiritual' with 'white.'"

But perhaps Wilson's story is merely a classic tragedy, the case of a fragile Apollonian soul exposed too quickly to a roiling Dionysian reality. As Schopenhauer put it in *The World as Will and Idea*, summarizing the breakdown of the individual

> BUT PERHAPS WILSON'S STORY IS MERELY A CLASSIC TRAGEDY, THE CASE OF **A FRAGILE APOLLONIAN SOUL** EXPOSED TOO QUICKLY TO A ROILING DIONYSIAN REALITY.

principle, of egoism, in the tragic figure: "The complete knowledge of the nature of the world, which has a quieting effect on the will, produces resignation, the surrender not merely of life, but of the very will to live." Through the ego death of LSD, Wilson's Apollonian veil was lifted. Like Hudson in *Seconds*, he "died" and was "reborn" into a new, Dionysian community of free will and unbounded pleasure to which his nature was ultimately unsuited. As in *Seconds*, it destroyed him. Both men end up "killed" by the very company that made them—Hudson by "rebirth" executives, Wilson by teenyboppers who grew up to be hippies.

Maybe the proof was already in the pudding. Describing a man caught in the veil of Maya (the Hindu goddess of illusion that Nietzsche relates to Apollo), Schopenhauer wrote: "Even as on an immense, raging sea, assailed by huge wave crests, a man sits in a little rowboat trusting his frail craft, so amidst the furi-

APPROPRIATELY, THIS RECORD ALSO CONTAINED THE HAUNTING, ELEGIAC "TILL I DIE," WILSON'S LAST TRULY **GREAT SONG**, IN WHICH HE REFLECTED ON THE DISINTE-GRATION OF HIS SELF.

ous torments of this world, the individual sits tranquilly, supported by the Principium individuationis and relying on it." Parks's lyric to the *Smile* masterpiece "Surf's Up" echoed this tenuous Apollonian state and seemingly urged Wilson to join the Dionysian spring:

Surf's up

Aboard a tidal wave

Come about hard and join

The young and often spring you gave

"Surf's Up" would not be released until 1971, in a collaged version from various sessions, on an album of the same name. Appropriately, this record also contained the haunting, elegiac "Till I Die," Wilson's last truly great song, in which he reflected on the disintegration of his self, post-*Smile*—his inability to hang on to his ego, his Apollonian craft, aboard the LSD-fueled, Dionysian tidal wave of 1967:

I'm a cork on the ocean

Floating over the raging sea

How deep is the ocean?

How deep is the ocean?

I lost my way

In the words of unlikely fan John Cale, who paid tribute to Wilson in song on his 1975 album *Slow Dazzle*, "I believe you, Mr. Wilson."

[RECOMMENDED LISTENING]

UNSURPASSED MASTERS VOL. 16-17 (1966-67), *The Smile Sessions/Smile* (Sea of Tunes) 4 CD bootleg

GOOD VIBRATIONS: THIRTY YEARS OF THE BEACH BOYS (Capitol) box set, discs 2 and 3

PET SOUNDS (Capitol)   ✳ ✳ ✳

anything goes

(An excerpt from the upcoming novel)

"There's this singer," my father said.

"Yeah?" I looked over, could only see the outline of his face in the dark, staring down the road ahead, into the pools of headlight.

"Over to East Nashville," he said, a little impatient, like we had already talked about this and I was being slow. "You want to go hear it?"

by Madison Smartt Bell

I took another look at him and figured, why not? See what other mysteries he had run up his sleeve.

He piloted me to the Woodland Street Bridge, and we crossed over the river. I had not hardly been over that way at all since I moved out from him, and when I looked down at the lights shining on the water, I started to feel kind of low. This sinking feeling got worse when I found out where we were going, which was a no-hoper roadhouse just a couple miles straight out Woodland Street from the bridge and downtown Nashville— no more than a long low shack with blacked-out windows, and straggling block letters in drippy white paint on the walls, telling about LIVE MUSIC and LADIES NIGHT and so on. I turned off the car and sat there listening to it tick and wondered what was giving me the weirds. The place wasn't that different from what you'd find downtown except it was too far off the beat to draw tourists. Aside from which it was a classic Black Cat, really. I'd played in a thousand places just like it.

I got out and made to pass the keys to Daddy across the roof of the car, but he waved them away.

"You hold them," he said.

We crossed the street toward the door of the bar, together but not too close, both of us feeling a little edgy I suppose. When we went inside I figured out what was bugging me. I had not been in there more than a time or two probably but I knew it as a place Daddy used to come home drunk from.

> I HAD NOT BEEN IN THERE MORE THAN A TIME OR TWO PROBABLY BUT I KNEW IT AS A PLACE DADDY USED TO COME HOME DRUNK FROM.

Inside was the usual Black Cat setup: bar with the beer signs and gag posters, a dozen or so wobbly tables and chairs, and toward the back two coin pool tables about the size of motel bathtubs. Place was about half full of people from the neighborhood, even a couple I could recognize from what used to be my street. The bandstand was just a corner of the room with some amps and a drum kit and a dust-crusted PA that looked like it probably didn't work. Nobody was playing the drums, but they had two longhairs with jail tats on their stringy arms knocking out an up-tempo blues on bass and guitar. In front of them was this woman with long dark halfway-matted hair, stone country-looking down to the floor-length gingham granny dress she had on. I sort of wanted to look at her feet to see if she was wearing shoes. But the first thing I noticed was she was so pregnant I figured she might have the baby when the band went on break. She wasn't singing anything yet; she was rocking on her heels and looking at the microphone in her hand like she expected it was gonna talk back to her. The way the mike cord waved around sort of reminded me of Perry with that snake.

Meanwhile Daddy was glad-handing his way through the room. Most people appeared to know him, including the bartender. I went over and took a long-neck Bud. The bartender looked at Daddy, who didn't say anything at first.

"Well, give me a goddamn O'Doul's," he said finally. The bartender chuckled at him as he paid.

We sat down at a free table; I crawled underneath and wedged a matchbook under one leg to stop it wobbling. When I came back up Daddy was pulling on his near-beer with kind of a sour expression on his face.

"You really quit drinking, huh?" I said.

"Yeah," Daddy said. "I been going to that AA."

I nodded. "You like it?"

"Hell no, I don't like it," Daddy said. The edge on his voice made me want to take a long step back, maybe keep on stepping. But after a second he appeared to calm down.

"It's better'n nothing," he said.

I kind of wanted to know more, but I couldn't seem to think of a question, much less whether I should ask it or not. It was uncomfortable there for about half a minute but then the mike popped and the country girl was singing.

Well I tole you purty babeh . . .
Such a long time ago . . .

I hitched my chair around pretty quick so I could see where that sound was coming from. She had a big voice, no mistake. If I closed my eyes I thought I could hear a little black in it. Whatever color, it was enough voice to fill the room, even without the mike, I thought. It even almost made you forget how lame the band was.

When she finished, somebody hollered out a request and she counted off and went into "You Ain't Woman Enough to Take My Man." I could hear more of a grit edge in her voice then, a mountain tone, with the longhair twanging on his beater Telecaster, but it was still a little bluesy along with that. Nice. She could have killed some of those old country tunes. I started to sort of wish that Perry was there to hear it. I leaned over to Daddy.

"What's her name?"

"Estelle," Daddy said into my ear, throwing the accent toward the front end of the name. "Estelle Cheatham."

Then for the next number she did this weird tune off the first Cowboy Junkies album—the one with "Blue Moon" spliced in for a bridge. And she came to that part of it, the moon came out of her mouth like a bubble blown in molten glass, shimmering all the colors of the rainbow, then breaking with a chime . . . I was broke out in gooseflesh all over, the hair on my arms standing straight up.

They closed out the set with that one. Estelle snapped the microphone back on this stand that was there and came over toward our table, lumbering 'cause she was so pregnant.

"Hidy, Wendell," she said to Daddy. "Thanks for coming out." She kind of cocked up her hip when she spoke to him, and I saw how she might be good-looking if she fixed herself up. Supposing she got the baby delivered, and did a little something about her hair . . . She had snapping green eyes, and funny dark coloring that really didn't go with that country twang in her voice. She was missing a front tooth and her smile was a little twisted to try and cover it up.

"Sound good tonight." Daddy pulled a thumb at me. "This is Jesse."

Estelle gave the crooked smile. "Hidy." She sounded more country talking than she did singing. It seemed like the cat had got my tongue—anyway all I came up with was a nod. She was so pregnant I thought the baby was going to jump out on the table any minute. It was hard to know how she could draw the breath to sing like she'd been doing.

Estelle kind of sighed and sat down in a straight-back chair between our table and the next one over. She told me the names of the couple there. I realized the girl looked enough like Estelle to be her sister, and her last name was Cheatham too. Rose-Lee Cheatham. The guy was another longhair looked like he sucked eggs for a living or something like that, Greg I think his name was. Estelle leaned back and crossed her legs, helping herself a little with a hand on an ankle. As a matter of fact she wasn't wearing shoes, just a pair of wooly red socks. She smiled around the missing tooth when she saw me looking.

"Feet swole up on me." She patted the baby through her gingham. "You know."

I looked at Rose-Lee to be looking somewhere else. She gave you an idea what Estelle might look like not pregnant—slender enough, but still filling out her orange tank top very nice, and without a bra, I couldn't help but notice. I'd have guessed her to be ten years younger than Estelle at least—she wasn't much over twenty anyway. Then again it was hard to tell how old Estelle really was by looking.

I knew I'd been staring too hard at Rose-Lee now when she gave me her version of the bad-teeth smile and scraped her chair around so I was mostly looking at her back. I felt like maybe old Greg was giving me the evil eye too, so I looked off at the bandstand, which was empty now. The two longhairs had hit the door fast when the set was done. Anxious to shoot up, I wouldn't have been surprised.

Daddy went to the bar and bought a round for both tables. Estelle took a beer and smoked herself a Marlboro Red. I guessed she wasn't too heavy into any pregnancy health regimes or anything like that. There was country on the jukebox. About fifteen minutes went by and Estelle started looking jumpy. She leaned over and tapped old Greg.

"Kin you go see about'm?" she said. It was funny, the difference of her talking voice from her singing one. Like if you heard Mick Jagger talking you would think he was some kind of an Englishman, but once he tunes up to sing you know he's a black man from the Mississippi Delta.

There was a click of pool balls from the coin tables behind us, and I heard somebody cuss his shot. Estelle settled back in her chair and fired up another cigarette. In a couple minutes Greg came back in trailing the longhair bass player. Dude was still more or less breathing, but he definitely looked a lot more relaxed than he had when he first went out.

"Whar's Tawmie?" Estelle wanted to know.

"Hanh?"

"Whar's Tawmie?" She stubbed out her cigarette so hard I thought it was going to go through the ashtray and the table altogether. At the same time I sort of had the idea this problem probably came up pretty regular.

"Cain't wake him up," bass player said. He sat down on a chair, very loose-limbed, and showed us the whites of his eyes.

"You cain't wake him up," Estelle said. "Well shit on far."

"Have you got a song list?" I heard myself say.

Estelle rounded on me with her green eyes sparking so hot it scared me. I wouldn't of wanted to be old Tawmie, whenever he did come to.

"Have you got a song list?" I said.

"Not really," she said. "We mostly just call'm out as we go. How come, kin you play guitar?"

"Sometimes I do," I said. I looked over at that Telecaster. Old Tawmie didn't have a stand

I WASN'T PLANNING ON SPENDING THE NIGHT AT HIS PLACE NO MATTER HOW PLEASANT THE EVENING HAD BEEN.

for the thing, he had just wedged it up against the wall. I almost had butterflies in my stomach, thinking about getting up there with her. "Why don't you just call me a few right now and we'll see which ones of them I know?"

Estelle stared at me for a second and then she nodded. Then she leaned across the other table with her arm swinging in this kind of slow lazy way and cracked the bass player on the jawbone with a slap you could have heard across the river.

"Hanh?" goes the bass player. He honestly didn't know she'd hit him.

"Git up thar," she told him. "You ain't done working yet."

We ended up turning out a decent couple of sets, in spite of some predictable problems with the rhythm section, which I solved by turning the dude's amp so low you couldn't hardly hear him. He didn't know the difference himself, but somehow he was able to keep up a kind of Quaalude walking bass—good enough, since I didn't feel required to solo much.

Estelle was long and strong on Bonnie Raitt covers, old stuff mostly—blues like "Kokomo" and "Women Be Wise" and "Crying Mercy," plus also the ballads: "Louise," "Any Day Woman," "Love Has No Pride." She made the rafters ring on that last one; I was damn near crying myself. She wouldn't do a straight country song unless somebody asked for it, otherwise it was always something with a twist. She had a little Dylan ("I Shall Be Released"), some Stones ("Wild Horses," "Beast of Burden"), and a fair amount of classic blues—damn if she didn't sing "Catfish," retooled for a woman's point of view.

When she was done she thanked me and offered me a piece of the tip jar, which I turned down. People had only been half listening and there wasn't a lot in it anyway. She'd sung herself out and her eyes had gone dull. Long time to be on your feet, I guess, that pregnant. I gave Daddy the nod to get out of there, 'cause I wanted to miss the part where she sorted things out with the other guitar guy. After lushing on near-beer all night long, he was probably more ready to leave than I was.

It had got to be one o'clock in the morning somehow by the time we hit the street. I starting wondering what was the program now. Was Daddy going to drive me an hour out to Perry's and then himself an hour back to town? I wasn't planning on spending the night at his place no matter how pleasant the evening had been.

I offered him the car key but he wouldn't take it. He jumped into the passenger seat, which didn't leave me much to do but get behind the wheel.

"You can just drop me by the house if you want to," he said.

"Drop you. What?"

Daddy looked out his window, the other way from me, and started talking kind of fast for him.

"The car's for you, Jesse. I wanted to do something for you. It's nothing to do with anything else. I just wanted to give you something."

He looked at me for a second, kind of crossways. "I wish you'd take it." Then he was staring out his window again.

If it had been Perry or Allston or just about anybody I'd of reached across and touched him on the shoulder. But I didn't do that now.

"Well, sure I'll take it," I said finally. "What kind of fool wouldn't?"

"That's all right, then." I heard him swallow. "It's late," he said. "I need to get home."

Ten minutes later I was pulling up the alley behind the house, a kind of crushed-looking old duplex. You couldn't tell anymore what color the paint on the back side used to be. The yard was all trashed up with car parts and stuff. The guy who lived in the other half had gathered around the bug light with some of his buddies. I cut the motor and sat for a minute.

"That's where Estelle and Rosie live at, right over yonder." Daddy pointed across the alley to a house that was dark now. "Heard her singing in the kitchen one time. That's how I come to know'm."

"Worth the trip," I said.

Daddy nodded and got out of the car.

"Hey Wendell." One of the guys around the bug light toasted him with a beer can.

"Title's in the glove box," Daddy told me. Then he was loping toward the back door and inside before I even said good night.

I cranked the car and drove back out to Perry's, not too fast, one eye out for the cops. Didn't hardly know what to think. Damn but it was a pretty car. I felt good about having it, that was simple enough, even if I didn't quite believe it yet. I thought I felt good about him giving it to me.

It was dark at Perry's when I got back. He was either asleep or had fired up one of the hulks and gone somewhere. The dogs came out to nose me, but they didn't bark. I wondered if Daddy showed up again would they bark at him. How many times would it take before they stopped? When I lay down it wasn't dogs I heard, but Estelle's voice ringing in my head. ▮

TALK-ING SAX WITH HER SON

FRANCINE PROSE—An Interview With-LEON MICHELS

Some years ago, in early January, I invited my son Leon—then fifteen or sixteen—to the local music mega-store, so we could treat ourselves to a CD or two, to celebrate the fact that our family had made it, alive and intact, through another so-called holiday season.

Leon asked: Does "CD or two" mean "boxed set?"

I said: No, it definitely did not. But what did he have in mind?

He said: James Brown. Mr. Dynamite.

James Brown? Reader, I bought it.

It's hard to describe the particular thrill of having an extremely—a certifiably—cool kid who loves the same music I loved when I was his age. And nothing could be more thrilling than the fact that he's outdone me. Not only does he listen to jazz and late-sixties soul. He plays it—and gets paid.

BY FRANCINE PROSE

e fell in love with jazz as a tiny kid, in elementary school, in upstate New York, where his hugely gifted and patient public-school music teacher organized a big band of fourth, fifth, and sixth graders playing surprisingly creditable versions of Duke Ellington and Count Basie. Our move back to the city was partly motivated by the fact that Leon's talent and passion for music had outgrown our rural neighborhood. Since tenth grade, Leon has been playing tenor sax in the horn section of a James Brown-style soul band, originally known as Sharon Jones and the Soul Providers, and now (after a name change having some obscure relation to new beginnings) Sharon Jones and the Dap-Kings. The band wears matching shiny jackets and skinny ties. Sharon, their lead singer, could be James Brown, only female—Ms. Dynamite—less narcissistic and controlling, a few years younger than I. Leon has also played with various big bands; years ago he got a one-night gig playing with a pickup big band that backed Harry Connick Jr. at a theater in Schenectady.

And he has his own group, the Mighty Imperials, in which he plays organ, and which sounds a little like the Meters reborn as four white kids. They play fairly regularly, in clubs, downtown, and on the Lower East Side. It's always a thrill to hear the bands play, though I'm old enough now that the late hours and the smoky clubs take a toll. Every time I take friends along, they want to trade in their lives—to give up whatever they've accomplished in return for a chance to

Francine and Leon

get up there and wail with the Dap-Kings or the Mighty Imperials.

If Leon's performance in math and French was often less than stellar, it was partly because he'd usually come home—just before exams—from touring England with his band. My view (which I can admit now that it's probably too late for some concerned social worker to intervene) was that, when he got older, having played in London's Jazz Café would seem a lot more exciting than having gotten a B+ in pre-algebra. This summer, he and the Dap-Kings spent a month playing an extended gig in Barcelona. When I caught up with Leon—using the occasion of this piece to ask a few questions I'd been wondering about—he was busy recording a concept album, a faux soundtrack for an imaginary seventies B-picture called *Pit Bull Mission: Kill!*, which he describes as a darker, nonporn version of the sorts of films in which Dirk Diggler starred in *Boogie Nights*.

Francine Prose: So what, exactly, do you like about late sixties and early seventies soul music?

Leon Michels: It's made for people to dance to and feel good, have a good time. It's not meant to be deeply intellectual, but when you analyze it, it's awesome. The way James Brown orchestrates a band sounds really simple, but he uses the most complex rhythms, and the way the instruments fit

together is intense. And the vocals are so emotional, practically like gospel, like church singing over serious drums. And the music is historically important—as important as Bob Dylan's. James Brown wrote all these black anthems, but the actual meaning behind them is kind of deluded. I have a lot of songs about Vietnam, people coming back from Vietnam, race and stuff. Actually, the only good music to come out of the early seventies is soul. Jazz is a different story. The early sixties were great: Miles Davis, Lee Morgan, Wayne Shorter, Coltrane. During the seventies jazz got sad, all those guys trying to make a buck, trying to cross over, and they just lost whatever it is that makes improvisational jazz good.

JAMES BROWN'S MUSIC IS HISTORICALLY IMPORTANT—AS IMPORTANT AS BOB DYLAN'S. JAMES BROWN WROTE ALL THESE BLACK ANTHEMS, BUT THE ACTUAL MEANING BEHIND THEM IS KIND OF DELUDED.

FP: What makes good improvisational jazz? How do you tell the difference between a great musician and some guy playing in a wedding band?

LM: When it's really good, you just love it, you can remember every lick. Like Cannnonball Adderly's solo on "Autumn Leaves." It's just obvious that the guy's a genius. The sound, the feeling he has, everything about it makes sense, one line follows perfectly from the last line, the sound is good, he accents the exact right thing. It just makes sense, the whole thing, in a way that some regular guy playing in a wedding band would never have thought of.

FP: Do you get nervous performing?

LP: Sometimes if I'm really relaxed while I'm playing, I'll come offstage and I'll be in the worst mood. The times I play best are when I'm so nervous I can't even form a thought. What's that thing Art Pepper said? Any musician who isn't nervous when he goes out to play probably isn't planning on playing anything worth playing. My theory about when you first start playing music and improvising, that's when you're likely the most creative that you'll probably ever be, though it may not be the best. Learning technique is important because it sounds better in the long run, but you have more stuff to think about and you start working your little habits in, and it becomes less free.

FP: What is it like to practice? I mean the process itself.

LM: You run scales, if there are chords in a song you run the scales to every chord. You run through the keys. Or maybe you take somebody else's solo and you run through that. The process is really tedious, but it's great when you get it. This is making me want to practice!

FP: And what are you working toward? How do you know when you get it?

LM: What you want are melodies that are connected from one chord to the next so that it all flows and makes sense and is interesting to the ear. I don't know. Basically, when you think about it, you realize it's this really sick process. That's why three-quarters of jazz musicians are really fucked up in the head.

FP: Why is that?

LM: Because you're trying to learn this extremely complicated language. You keep improving but at the same time you keep thinking: This is going to take so long! It takes so much fucking time!

FP: But Leon, you're just talking about art.

LM: Yeah, but jazz is different from any other art. I mean, after you go through that first really creative period when you don't know anything, then you can't even worry about being creative until you've got the technique down. And after that, being creative almost takes a backseat until you figure out what you want to say. I know these musicians who are fifty years old and they're still tortured, practicing.

FP: Fifty? Yikes! So how come you're not listening to what most other kids are listening to?

LM: Because it's mostly crap. The whole business is so cutthroat, musicians have got to make money or else it's all over. And you can hear it in the music. A lot of the records I really like—all these 45s from the seventies I collect—they were made by some guy who had 150 bucks and went into a studio just to have it on a record. Radiohead and most of the new bands, art music—it just sucks. The way they produce the albums and record it—everything is so finely tuned, it sounds like a machine. When they made Blue Note records, Rudy Van Gelder put two mikes in his living room, and the musicians just played. Now they've got three-thousand-dollar microphones on every part of the drum and it just sounds all crisp, like a computer. Some of the rap they're doing now, there's this whole underground rap scene. It's close to what people were doing ten years ago. I like the approach they're taking to the music business—putting out music they like

that's not meant to appeal to teenyboppers and make a million dollars.

FP: What would be your dream band if you could put it together?

LM: Dream band? I have five of them. I'd like to have a twelve-piece James Brown-type band. A jazz band like an early sixties Miles Davis band. An eighteen-piece Afrobeat orchestra. Some huge Latin jazz band—Dizzy Gillespie kind of thing. Or maybe some combination. You can't tell. You get a band to play for a while, and then it goes in the direction it goes. You want to do something new, but not too new. New bands trying to be innovative sometimes wind up sounding forced and stupid.

FP: Do you think about music even when you're not playing?

LM: I hear music in my head all the time, it's sort of like daydreaming. It's a way to entertain yourself. The reason I love to fall asleep listening to music is that I dream about music. I dream I'm playing the most awesome song ever, and when I wake up, I can almost remember it. I can't really—but I know I dreamed about the coolest song. When I had that 5-CD changer, I could listen to music all night. One night, I fell asleep listening to Horace Silver's "Judy Grind." I know the sax solo by heart. And I dreamed I was playing it—because I knew every note. 🎺

White Bottom Blues

by

Judith Hall

I done showed y'all my black bottom
You ought to learn that dance. —Gertrude "Ma" Rainey, 1928

Girl: Give me, anywhere's around, the lowest room.
Anywhere's around, the lowest room.
Give me anywhere's around the lowest room.

Chorus: —Ma done showed y'all her black bottom.
Is that the best you got to show? Ain't no particlar
Bottom's dream, oblivious as joy. —Ma, you helpin her?

—She'll learn.—She stings not, neither do she stomp.
Girl: Humor me. He said I was his Great Depression. Hon,
I CRASHED! Worked my buttered butt to gleaming. Chump

Burlesque for pocket change, on my knees, Pa. Ha!
Abstract enough for boys in the back room?
They want a BRA & PANTIES matched. OFFD? How'm I doin?

Man: [Spoken, as to Ma] *Ah, do it. Do it, honey!*
Look out now, you's gettin kinda rough, girl! You bet' be
Yourself, now, careful, now, not too strong, not too strong, honey!

Girl: Every Great Depression needs a Star-Spangled Banner.
Every misery, a thrill. I know a bomb, she's burstin backstairs,
Got his rocket's red glare. His flag, it's still there.

What do I care? I FEEL GOOD, banged from way back.
Chorus: —She slums, but lonesome cruisin ain't carousin, ain't
What Ma would do. Ain't assimilated. Mo' appropriated.

Opportune. Asinine in the best of times, and in the worst,
Divin in, ostensible witness blues?—Ain't that.—Worse—
Let her be.—Ma?—Only so much some can learn.

Girl: I can learn. Look, a big white bottom, home and brave.
Chorus:—Humorous. Humorous.—Hush now. Won't matter days.
Don't worry years.—You know she'll have the last word.

Girl: Lifted up, last, first, MADAM WHITE BOTTOM TO YOU.
Bottom's up! How'm I doin, Ma? Ma: You'll learn.
Some folks got to work that hard for someone else's blues.

silence

in the age of noise

by geoffrey o'brien

Recording CHANGED EVERYTHING. It beat time at its own game.

Permanent oldies; oldies on night call; the buttons pushed twenty-four-seven, as long as somebody is left alive to respond.

Maybe longer: even after the end of the world in *On the Beach* there was a record that kept spinning around for no one.

I will know that old age has arrived when even the oldies are unfamiliar songs of younger generations, and "Do Wah Diddy Diddy" and "Back Stabbers" are stashed away in the archive along with "Whispering" and "Alice Blue Gown," the music of a past that there is no one left to be reminded of.

minate duration. The music expresses whatever you care to project onto it. It is at once nowhere and everywhere.

But it is scarcely on the street. The dancers and drummers in the plaza have mostly gone away, although a few find shelter in the subway. Even the boom

> { Remember when there were happy songs, sad songs? We have moved into a new country, of prolonged and indeterminate duration. }

It is a final indignity, the Memory Lane Massacre. You wake up in a world where you can't identify or even distinguish among any of the songs; where in fact they aren't "songs" anymore but endless strips of sound, with no beginning or end.

Remember endings? We thought we liked them. Or at least they somehow seemed necessary. How else do you deal with the fact that the music has to stop sometime? The instruments get louder; or the singer starts to improvise more freely and excitedly; or the chorus comes in for a final reprise. It's your signal to say goodbye to the song and all it has meant to you, until the next time.

Remember when there were happy songs, sad songs? We have moved into a new country, of prolonged and indeter-

boxes grow quiet in the age of headphones, where music can be piped hygienically and noiselessly into each individual head without disrupting the public sphere.

Most of those listening to music on records no longer know how to play it. Even on many of the records themselves, people do not play except in the sense of making collages of earlier records. ("Do you know how many musicians have been put out of work by digital technology?" "No, but hum a few bars and I'll sample it.")

Perhaps it began when new records positioned themselves as commentary on earlier records. ("All of punk music," the earnest radio commentator—Gary Thrall, ex-bass player for the early-eighties band the Simplistics—is suggesting, "is nothing more than an extended footnote to certain recordings by the Who, which were themselves an oblique commentary on surf music, while at the same time all of them, the surfers, the Who, the punks, were listening to the same James Brown records.") Perhaps it began when the concept began to change from record as copy of live performance to record as thing-in-itself. But the wedge was already being driven in with the first recording.

Now the computers come equipped with machinery for creating masterpieces of sampling. Design your own trance. Maybe it will even drown out the hums and white-noise signals of the machinery on which you design it, or the city—itself rapidly undergoing a digital transformation—in which you play it back.

The push-button living we were promised in the fifties—the doors opening and lights going on by themselves, the tone arm dropping the needle onto Mantovani's Immortal Classics at a preselected volume—has pretty much arrived. Even if we don't yet live in the fully operational "smart house," we pass from smart city to smart city through smart airports, watching smart television and listening to smart music machines.

The Russian inventor Theremin created not only the electronic instrument that bears his name but a range of prototypes for the world we live in: doors that open and close automatically, advertisements that switch on when approached by humans, security alarms sensitive to movement, surveillance devices capable of penetrating the U.S. embassy in Moscow.

Music was fed, in the ancient times that ended ten or twelve years ago, by the human scene around it. There was no way of getting around musicians, and all the mess and confusion pertaining to them.

Records, true to the spirit of all modern conveniences, provide the music without the scene. At the very least there is then no need to wait for the musicians to show up, or warm up, or get in the mood, or accommodate themselves to the listeners' more or less inarticulate desires.

And now the record makers—fulfilling an old dream—can dispense with musicians altogether, as if thereby to get at the music without having to deal with intermediaries. Eliminate the factor of human error, so to speak, all those flaws of character or inherent biases that get in the way, the awkward aftereffects of habit and experience.

The culture that gives us these things wants above all to satisfy a longing for human contact that persists stubbornly, even among those who little by little have gotten hooked on life with as little such contact as possible. It's a tough order to fill, unless the customer agrees to be contented with an illusion of contact. After that— once the replica has been accepted as a full equivalent of its original—the possibilities are endless. It's a matter of training.

Our childhood was a preparation for vicarious living. Gradually we were made accustomed to music without instruments, even without instrumentalists. In return for whatever loss that might entail, we get to keep all the music forever. Playback is instant and on demand. As for the rest of it, how much did you really care? You have been liberated from all that smoke, all that waiting around.

Wherever we are we find ourselves pushing many buttons, until the prehensile thumb begins to feel as superfluous as the appendix. (We begin to glimpse the end of handling.) Gradually music becomes a mere substitute for silence, a sonic blanket designed to make a bit more tolerable an environment where the little noises of the little machines never stop. There are CD players that can be programmed for thirty-six hours of continuous play, and that is surely only a beginning.

Music drowns out sound, or drowns out self. When the bass makes your bones vibrate it's the most intimate possible invasion.

The new phone beeps are indistinguishable: is it sounding in the TV movie or in the room itself, and is there a difference? Sound negates sense of place. "I'm on the train": no, he isn't, he's on the phone.

A guy walks briskly along the avenue talking into his cell phone: "You're so indifferent." Or was it: "It's someone different"? The city itself is the switchboard where the operators are subjected to a thousand different randomly crisscrossing conversations at the same time.

It seems like a long time ago that rock and roll made it hard to have conversations in bars, and when booming speakers made it impossible to talk at parties or clubs. We got used to this slowly. Was it sometime in the sixties or seventies that it became normal not to be able to hear what anyone was saying, and not to care? ("A person can't hear himself think in here." "That's the idea, baby.")

At some point music becomes not the cure but the ailment. Music as annoyance: the hip-hop at deafening volume in the adjacent passenger's headphones; the music from the cruise ships that pass by

{ At suburban malls Beethoven and Brahms are played over the PA systems to drive away the teenage loiterers. }

the harbor apartment window all night long (the salsa boat, the disco boat, the Céline Dion boat); the pounding electronic themes of TV news shows, exploring the aesthetic of the emergency beeper (an ultimate vulgarization of the music of Philip Glass?); the mix tape of New Age synthesizer music without which your tofu would not be complete. But we were told of this long ago. In Fritz Lang's 1952 movie *The Blue Gardenia*, Richard Conte and his partner sit in a restaurant talking about a murder, and the partner is startled by the sudden intrusion of an invisible orchestra: "What's that?" "Music. Canned. They can everything nowadays."

During Operation Just Cause, American troops lay siege to the Vatican embassy in Panama City, where General Manuel Noriega had taken refuge. On the third day they brought in the psych-warfare team to wear down his resistance by means of painfully loud, indefinitely prolonged sonic bombardment with mix tapes designed to be as irritating as possible, everything from heavy metal to *Barry Manilow's Greatest Hits*. (The playlist also

included, with a whimsy possibly lost on the general, Martha and the Vandellas' "Nowhere to Run" and Linda Ronstadt's "You're No Good.") Conversely, police played the favorite records of an armed and mentally troubled woman barricaded in her home in an effort to tranquilize her by restoring a sense of familiar reality. The playlist included *Barry Manilow's Greatest Hits*.

At suburban malls Beethoven and Brahms are played over the PA systems to drive away the teenage loiterers, who find the music oppressive.

Records can become a torture device anywhere at all. Tourists at a restaurant overlooking Lake Baikal are subjected to hideously distorted military music played at top volume on a broken-down phonograph, the employees apparently oblivious to the deafening sound while the Westerners try to focus on their bumpers of vodka and heaping platters of goulash. A Japanese main street at Christmastime becomes a traffic jam of competing carols and seasonal favorites, "Frosty the Snowman" and "Silent Night" and "Jingle Bell Rock" simultaneously from different storefronts at the same bludgeoning volume.

The final punishment—the delayed punishment—comes when no music at all is playing. This is the moment—it's three o'clock by the luminous dial that never shuts off—when it begins to look as if you'll be up all night auditioning for Pride of the Insomniacs as you relive each bar of a hated tune that repeats and repeats, a perpetual-motion machine whose circular structure is sometimes even compounded by the lyrics themselves: "The Music Goes Round and Round," "Raindrops Keep Falling on My Head." "Big wheel keep on turning," indeed.

In Charles Williams's noir novel *All the Way* (1956), the insidiously circular 1934 hit "The Music Goes Round and Round"—a record whose effect is something like being strapped to a wooden horse on a carousel that will never stop—is used to drive someone mad. The prospective victim's brother committed suicide many years earlier after locking himself in his room and playing "The Music Goes Round and Round" repeatedly for days. Now an ingenious conspirator reminds him of it by calling up and playing the record over the phone. The whole book amounts to an arcane piece of music criticism. That Williams himself later committed suicide gives the joke an unexpected gravity.

Hell is an oldies station that cannot be tuned out.

Wasn't there a scary TV show like that, on *Panic Theater* or some such program? The radio had no controls, the sound got louder and louder, and when the tenant went to open the window to make contact with the outside world there were only thick metal panels bolted into place?

A car alarm echoes through the urban canyon, symbol of a maddening reality that there is no way to shut out. Within the skull, as its counterpart, there is what cannot be shut off: the five thousandth chorus of "Nice and Easy," not actually a chorus but merely the bar and a half that got stuck, a bit of well-crafted sonic shrapnel.

Composers often describe being kept awake by their own melodies until they are forced to get out of bed and write them down. At some moments it becomes clear to the victimized listener that the songwriter has escaped from insomnia by inflicting it on someone else. "Put the tune in *their* brains!"

There are songs that should have a warning attached to them: Casual Listening May Result in Melody Burn. They appear scientifically designed to cause suffering, and are even proud of it, proclaiming the intention brazenly like the Electric Light Orchestra's "Can't Get It out of My Head."

Horror of horrors: These recursive structures pull their legs in after themselves and curl around back to the first note. Such songs suggest what a terrible thing eternity might be. Even in dreams the gears continue their infernal creaking, and it scarcely surprises when the doorkeeper of an oneiric tavern—the one to which you had just barely been admitted—bursts into the same refrain to wake you.

There was always music designed to make sure you couldn't hear, or even imagine, any other music. All together now: "The East Is Red," the "Horst Wessel Lied," the "Agincourt Song," the Latin hymn of the Teutonic knights making ready to devastate the people of Novgorod in Eisenstein's *Alexander Nevsky*. Or for that matter the marching song of the Russian peasants spontaneously rising up against the invader, dropping their farming tools, grabbing spears, and heading down the road to the recruiting center with the Prokofiev music to inspire them. Whether it's the Seventh Cavalry riding through

{ A wrathful Tibetan deity singing about the end of the world, except that he has forgone his usual conduit of deep-chanting monks and weirdly recruited Barry Manilow for the purpose? }

Or is not something scarier at work, the activation of an embedded voodoo code that takes possession of any available brain matter? "Babalu" colonizing the hearer through the essentially passive intermediation of Desi Arnaz? A wrathful Tibetan deity singing about the end of the world whether you want to hear it or not, except that he has forgone his usual conduit of deep-chanting monks and weirdly recruited Barry Manilow for the purpose?

Monument Valley to the tune of "The Girl I Left Behind," or the Japanese office workers singing the company song at their desks as a prelude to group calisthenics, there is nothing like a song to give an illusion of purposeful activity. The battle of anthems in *La Grande Illusion* and *Casablanca*, of Zulu chant against Welsh choir in *Zulu*, reduces war to a matter of competing sound systems. Nothing, finally, is as terrifying as the notion of music that cannot be deselected: the anthem of the army that is marching to destroy you, the hymns of the parishioners who are preparing to watch you burn. When you get to pick the music you can change history.

A lone flute from the woods signals a last inextinguishable spark of enemy resistance.

Useless to try to escape from it. It knocks unbidden and forces its patterns on us, forces us to live in the time it beats out, inhabits even its absence.

Music is such a grammar that even with all the notes taken out it still superimposes its structures on us.

{ Because of people, silence is disappearing from the planet. We are the Noise-Bringers. }

Shut the music machine off. Turn out the last light. Silence and darkness. Now it begins, the real racket: distant slams and hoots, motorcyclist revving up at the on-ramp, chamber symphony of foghorns, pleasure boat rounding the cove with a blast of salsa out on the water where the glittering lights are, elevator doors slamming open and shut as drunk or squabbling couples come home, small heavy object knocked over by household pet on the floor directly above, deep hum (itself nearly Tibetan) of refrigerator, infomercial about hair implants being watched by the insomniac next door, crackling of electricals, noise of chairs and desks that somehow creak when they are unoccupied, buffeting of window by air currents, gradual uncrumpling of the wad of paper thrown into a basket half an hour ago, like a high-volume recorded transcription of a flower opening, rattle of air against glass, noise of head nestling against pillow and of bed

"It is the Death Song": the melancholy, inexorable tune that General Santa Anna had his musicians play day and night outside the Alamo until the siege was over, at least according to the screenplay of *Rio Bravo*. The bad guys re-created it with a local mariachi band to wage psychological warfare on John Wayne, Dean Martin, and Walter Brennan, cooped up in a jailhouse with a town full of vicious outlaws surrounding them. Gets to you.

But there will always be an old coot like Brennan to start humming along— "Dang, I'm startin' to kinda like that tune"—just like Hank Worden, as old Mose Harper in *The Searchers*, going into his travesty of a Comanche war dance at the most inappropriate moment, on the edge of massacre.

frame adjusting to the body that stretches on it, noise of breath, noise of bones. No getting out of this symphony alive.

Under all, even if everything else were shut out, is the noise of the inner workshop of the body, echoing faintly from the deepest chambers, as if a thousand workers clambered over pulleys and cauldrons, chanting all the while their midnight work song. They are the slaves of time, bald gnomes out of a Brothers Grimm story or a Wagnerian opera, stirring with giant ladles and hauling cinder blocks while they keep the hum going. They labor all night in anticipation of the silence of that future day when they will be allowed finally to rest. Meanwhile they strike up another chorus. It's that Manilow thing again. It is the Death Song. When they are finished with their work the song will stop.

Silence is what was just interrupted. It's been like that always. That is how you know the silence was perceptible a moment earlier, a moment before the godlike howling of the noon whistle in a quiet suburb, a moment before the roar of a motorboat on a mountain lake in the days when such roars were new: "You have no idea how peaceful it was before those damn things were invented." "Somebody ought to make a law about

it. It's getting so you can't hear yourself think anymore."

Because of people, silence is disappearing from the planet. We are the Noise-Bringers. (Our boom box is bigger than the boom box of linnet or cicada.)

In their Himalayan fastnesses the saddhus practicing their austerities hear the jets roar by. A man travels around the world with a tape recorder trying to find a soundtrack uninterrupted by some form of machinery. He has trouble managing more than fifteen minutes of it, anywhere.

We tell time by noise. Silence appalls most by its suggestion that time is absent.

A length of audiotape, gathering sound to its surface as it uncoils: that is a lifetime. If not stored at excessive temperatures, and if the mylar coating resists any tendencies toward breaking or crumpling or warping, it is good for a program of extended duration at optimal dynamic levels. As long as it can be played back—as long as the encoded information does not wear away—the tape will be a history of what was heard.

Everything enters there. The noises register the persistence of life as on a seismograph. The tiniest shudder is identifiable by its characteristic acoustical marking.

On this tape there is no such thing as dead air. Even the pauses make noise.

Sounds erase sounds, voices bury voices. The single lifetime is this field of interruptions, a carpet of distinct scratches and whistles. Here a deep hoot, there a high feverish chattering; here a guttural murmur of satisfaction as the hungry are being fed, there plaintive distant cry as the mother calls her children from play at sunset, her growing anxiety modulating into an audible change of register. Everything barges in, everything slams the door.

Sound penetrates where it wishes regardless of what anybody wants or doesn't want. The shape of a personality gets caught—like a sleeve on a bramble—in a single phrase, a single sigh, the lover's raucous gasp, the suicide's ironic murmur.

A small but crucial event is encapsulated in the almost childish giggle, barely held in control, of the pilot who has just recognized a technical problem a moment before takeoff and thereby saved himself and his passengers.

After someone dies his voice is what persists, an auditory signature in the inner ear, the timbre exactly sustained. A life extends just as long as that peculiar accent can be played back by the person in whom it was recorded.

All of it music, all the time: the roar of empty countryside, the terror of uninhabited night, the hiss and clack of bare boughs set upon by wind. It lacks only a little orchestration, a little sweetening, the human touch.

We go looking for silence—the imagined silence, silence the pure. But what

{ There is a different kind of silence, the silence of those places where no music ever plays, filled as they may be with every other kind of noise. }

is silence, if not the outward manifestation of absence, disappearance, death? It can be imagined in dreams: the discovery of the emptied house, in the wake of massacre or pestilence or economic catastrophe.

"Stilled the laughter, stilled the weeping." Years later the exile returns to the abandoned cottage, the deserted village. "No sound was there but the hissing of the wind in the winter trees."

There is a different kind of silence, the silence of those places where no music ever plays, filled as they may be with every other kind of noise. If you are in one of them it is the only place, and for the rest of life you will cling to music as to a haven from that mute prohibition. (You will dream of the musical penthouse within whose soundproofed walls there is a permanent outpouring of rumba music, the satin suite made for love and champagne and top-flight orchestral arrangements.) It might have been a house with no radio or record player, or where the radio and record player were never turned on; without a piano, or where the piano was permanently draped in a dustcover. Here music died, or something died of

Noise of slaps, clatter of garbage-pail lids. In some yard cluttered with broken glass, where a tenant coughs behind the curtain, uncounted years of noons and midnights collapse into a single moment, in a place where even music wouldn't help.

So turn it up as loud as possible. Open the windows while you're at it, put the speaker on the fire escape. When you hear music you know you're still alive, and the others might as well know too. Otherwise it's hard to be sure.

As death approaches, even the *mention* of Bach or Mozart can be a profound palliative, however brief the effect. To evoke their music is to bring timelessness and freedom into a room defined by time and necessity.

{ The weight of that absence gave a sense of how devastating a single chord would be. }

which music would be too painful a reminder. The weight of that absence gave a sense of how devastating a single chord would be, if a child should stray in and start pounding randomly on the piano. With what panic would nursemaid or maiden aunt come rushing out to hiss, "Don't do that, dear! You'll wake them!"

Or, perhaps: "Turn that goddamn noise off!"

In the wilderness, in a trance in the hospital, in the dead calm of mid-ocean, an encroaching silence lurks around you. Or would, but for the human ingenuity that puts a set of speakers near every IV tank and on every airplane. It's okay, it's going to be fine: there's an orchestral tribute to Andrew Lloyd Webber on channel 23, a brave thin piping sound. Outside the music's limits a mechanical groan thickens, the roar of ambient chaos.

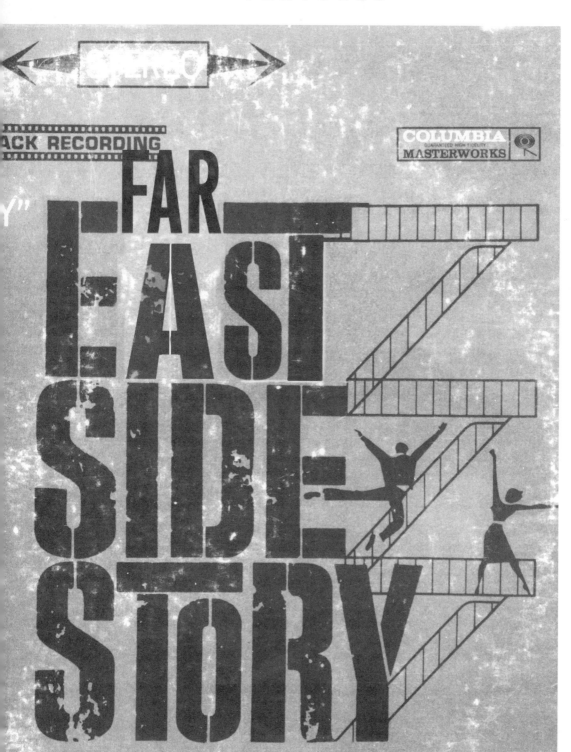

How the Jets and Sharks Rumbled in Tiananmen Square

I was born in 1962, which made me just old enough to catch the last few of my father's Young People's Concerts with the New York Philharmonic. I remember little about the actual concert experience, save being scolded by a cameraman for flailing around in my seat, i.e., mimicking Daddy on the podium. I do remember watching the shows on television and feeling mighty proud. More substantial memories of those glory days belong to my older sister and brother, Jamie and Alexander, who were five and three years old respectively, just as Daddy assumed the directorship at the Philharmonic in 1957. They remember getting up with him at 5 AM to drive over to Philharmonic Hall for the camera rehearsal; the mad re-write sessions before air-time; the tense excitement of the live broadcast. Mostly, they remember the thrill of hearing their favorite pop culture icons turn up in the scripts. For over a decade, Jamie and Alexander were uncredited collaborators on television's signature music education series. Thanks to them, Elvis, the Beatles, the Kinks, the Lone Ranger and Superman all served in the employ of Leonard Bernstein's musical pedagogy.

Many people mistakenly believe that the Young People's Concerts were a Bernstein invention. Actually, they had been a New York Philharmonic fixture for decades but had mainly benefited the children of the city's elite. When my father took over the orchestra, he buttonholed William Paley, chairman of CBS and conveniently on the Philharmonic's Board of Directors, to insist that the shows be televised. Paley recognized the idea's potential and seized the moment: for a country coming to terms with its socioeconomic inequities, this was a programming masterstroke. Daddy had known the power of television for years, ever since he had stood on a giant painted score of Beethoven's Fifth Symphony and explained the intricacies of that piece to the "Omnibus" audience. Now, he would multiply his viewers to include his favorite audience of all: kids.

Which came first: the lesson or the fun? For Daddy, or "LB" as we refer to him now, the answer was always "both". He worshipped at the shrines of Apollo and Dionysus equally. In one program called "What Makes Music Symphonic?" he explained the fundamentals of symphonic development with standard

by Nina Bernstein Simmons

schoolhouse delivery and then proceeded to illustrate with a few verses of "I'm All Shook Up." This was not just sugar-coating a pill; the lesson had integrity and the kids were, needless to say, enrapt.

It would seem, looking at his successors, that this balance is harder to attain than one would think. Those with proper respect for the material often forget the age of their listeners; those who would not bore their young audience with dry facts condescend with clowning. As for public television nowadays, programming marches to the marketer's drum every bit as much as commercial television does. Even the original Young People's Concerts series utterly fails today's broadcast marketing profile. After all, who can compete with Barney? And to think: the Young People's Concerts were once broadcast nationally at prime time.

Today, American symphony orchestras, feeling like dinosaurs, worry about where their future audiences will come from. Altruism aside, they need to educate their communities' young people about classical music just to save themselves from extinction. "Where are the Bernsteins of today?" they ask. Eventually, the question reached us from LB's music publishers, Boosey and Hawkes. American orchestras were starved for fun, compelling children's concerts to jump start their weak educational programs. B & H was certain that a concert for young people featuring

LB's music would galvanize the audience as well as promote the composer's catalog. What did we, LB's family, think of such an idea? My sister, Jamie, finding the circularity of the situation irresistible, volunteered to write the concert herself. And thus, the *Bernstein Beat* was born.

Jamie is a fine writer and a musician in her own right, but she would be the first to admit her limitations where musicology is concerned. With this in mind, she enlisted the help of conductor Michael Barrett, whose honorary membership in our family dates back to the 1980s when he studied with our father. Michael not only possessed the necessary Apollonian qualities, but his boyish, Dionysian sensibilities suited the job perfectly. Over the course of two years, Jamie and Michael developed an all-Bernstein concert about rhythm that asked the musical question "What makes music dance?" With Michael on the podium and Jamie as narrator, they came pretty close to emulating the old magic: kids ate it up, and the concert took off. They were a hit in Salt Lake City, San Francisco, San Antonio and Washington, D.C. Then, when requests arrived for translations for foreign performances, things started getting interesting.

An invitation came from the Beijing Music Festival to perform the concert with the China National Symphony in October 2000. At this point I piped up: There was a film there, and I was going to make it. And so it came to pass that I traveled to China last year and became a seat-of-my-pants filmmaker overnight.

. . . .

During the Cultural Revolution, Chinese authorities deemed Western music counterrevolutionary—and therefore criminal. Scores, record collections, and instruments were all destroyed, and their owners severely punished. Professors of classical music fared worst of all. In the 1981 documentary *From Mao to Mozart*, the head of the Shanghai Conservatory tells of his two-year sentence in an airless closet over the building's septic tank. More remarkable than his survival is the fact that he recounts this nightmare from his office at the conservatory, where he presides once again, teaching the beloved music that he refused to abjure. As he recounts the saga, his face is at once disillusioned, hopeful, and strongly guarded, which pretty much sums up the spirit of China itself at that moment. With the scars of the Cultural Revolution still raw, the West, the Foreign Devil itself, was offering a friendly hand. No one could have predicted the extent to which China would trust that gesture. Now, a full generation later, the handshake has turned into a full embrace. Or so it would seem to the casual tourist.

At the Beijing airport we were greeted by a giant, toothy Arnold Schwartzeneg-

ger advertising, I think, Gillette razors. The taxi ride to the hotel contradicted every image of China we had grown up with. The legendary phalanxes of bicycles had given way to an equivalent legion of cars, all spewing leaded fumes into the dense yellow air. The architecture along the four-lane boulevard proclaimed sensational wealth and modernity and looked suspiciously like São Paulo or even Houston. The hotel itself, appropriately named the China World, occupied the better part of five blocks and ascended thirty stories. It boasted two subterranean malls where you could sip a Starbucks coffee, buy a new Spalding six-iron or a Prada dress, and then bowl a few frames if Beijing left you otherwise uninspired.

An invitation came from the Beijing Music Festival to perform the concert with the China National Symphony.

Given Beijing's evident surrender to Western culture, our expectations for the China National Symphony orchestra were high. Apparently, so were those of the Beijing Music Festival, for they had scheduled a second, evening concert in addition to the *Bernstein Beat*. Although the two concerts would share a good deal of music, the second show would also feature a considerable number of Bernstein show tunes, sung by two Chinese singers in addition to four American singers who had flown over with us. It was a tremendous amount of music to prepare in three days. Michael strode into the rehearsal hall that Wednesday morning with his usual vitality, eager to get started. We had assumed that with the exception of the principal tunes from *West Side Story*, LB's music would be new to the Chinese orchestra. And so to give them a head start, we had sent them the orchestral parts a few weeks before. Unfortunately, the shipping crate had sat unopened until that day.

The first piece to be rehearsed was "Three Dance Episodes from *On the Town*," an exuberant, jazzy hodgepodge of styles and rhythms that evoke New York in the 1940s. Even world-class orchestras need coaching on how to peform this playful, quirky piece: It's wildly syncopated, with changeable moods and specific textures. In most cases, though, professional musicians have a broad base of cultural knowledge working alongside their formal training, a common stylistic lingua franca that allows a conductor to say to any clarinetist anywhere: "That's too Benny Goodman. Can you make it seedier?" In the case of the China National Symphony, such a suggestion would not only have been meaningless, but it became instantly clear that the entire jazz idiom lay outside their scope of knowledge. It had simply never entered their ears. And neither, by the way, had the Latin polyrhythms that play such a central role in the *West Side Story* sections of the *Bernstein Beat* concert.

How could these conservatory-trained musicians—the premier orchestra in all of the People's Republic of China—have such limited musical exposure? What happened to the Big Handshake? Hadn't Mao given way to Mozart? In time, we learned that yes, Mozart had been forgiven, along with the standard pantheon of the classical and romantic periods. But the twentieth century had scarcely earned a nod: a smattering of Debussy and Ravel, but no Stravinsky, no Mahler, no Shostakovitch, no Ellington, no Copland. And now, suddenly, Bernstein? No wonder they were mystified.

The "Cool" fugue from *West Side Story* takes the bebop jazz style to symphonic heights. Its principal theme ("Boy, boy, crazy boy / Get cool Boy" when it is sung) is played first by the celli. The music is printed in symmetrical eighth notes and the tempo marker says, "swung": no further explanation necessary. But a cellist who does not know what "swung" means and has never heard "Swing" in the first place will play those eighth notes as written. And what will come out is a stately Maoist march to the tune of "Cool."

Leonard Bernstein with his daughter, Jamie, at a New York Philharmonic rehearsal, c. 1962.

It became instantly clear that the entire jazz idiom lay outside their scope of knowledge. It had simply never entered their ears. And neither, by the way, had the Latin polyrhythms that play such a central role in the **West Side Story** sections of the **Bernstein Beat** concert.

As each section of the orchestra entered the piece, Jamie sat very still and straight, willing them with all her being to swing, much as a frightened passenger wills an aircraft to fly. As for Michael, his role demanded a more assertive response. He set about teaching the orchestra how to play jazz, an enterprise he referred to later as "dentistry." Taking advice from LB's 1958 television program "The Art of Conducting," Michael used any means necessary to get the orchestra to play: "A conductor must exalt his orchestra, lift them, start their adrenaline pouring— either by pleading, demanding or raging, it doesn't matter," says LB. And so it went for three grueling days as the musicians got a crash course in pan-American rhythm and style.

Tempers ran high. No one had told Michael that the Chinese respond aversely to direct criticism, as it causes "loss of face." Consequently, Michael's efforts only antagonized the orchestra until he learned to mold his critiques into tortured shapes of praise. "Trombones—that's coming along nicely. Keep practicing that figure at home." But even so, he waged an uphill battle. Periodically, he would cue an instrument's entrance only to discover that the player in question had left the room. After the fifth or sixth occurrence, Michael finally lost all delicacy and said, "You would be fired for this in the United States!" We prayed that the interpreter had the good sense to leave that untranslated. The truth was, as there was no librarian, parts were often left off the players' stands by mistake, causing them to think they were not needed for that piece. They'd go out for an innocent smoke only to be dragged back in to face an apoplectic maestro.

As for the Chinese singers, they had prepared their parts as well as they could in advance of rehearsals. But again, without knowledge of the Broadway singing style, they brought a Wagnerian sensibility to bear on their *West Side Story* roles. Furthermore, their teachers had failed to provide any guidance at all on pronunciation or meaning. So while Michael walked them through the stylistic looking glass, Jamie gamely coached them on such phrases as "I'll drive a Buick through San Juan" and "sperm to worm."

At the close of the second day, Michael was in serious doubt about whether the orchestra would be able to play all of both programs. Should he cut his losses or press them harder? Sensing a moment of truth, the orchestra offered him more rehearsal time and with the exception of the brutal scherzo from the *Jeremiah* Sym-

phony, the decision was made to play everything as scheduled.

That evening, feeling weary and depressed, we were taken to a Peking Opera "nostalgia restaurant" near the Forbidden City. Many restaurants in China now have nostalgia themes. Some are half-ironic shrines to Mao featuring the signature dingy decor of the day. Others pay nostalgic tribute to the Cultural Revolution, serving the unspeakable fare that sustained China's starving population through those dreadful years. This one celebrated the heyday of the Peking Opera in all its opulence. We declined a rickshaw ride from the parking lot and walked into a colossal, roaring hall that was in the midst of dinner service for easily two hundred people. All the way down at one end was a small stage upon which a woman in bright yellow silk performed a karaoke rendition of a classic aria from Peking Opera. Her high-pitched nasal wailing entered the microphone, traveled through a powerful amplifier, and blasted out of twenty giant speakers hung throughout the room. To our ennervated, jet-lagged brains, the music was not just indecipherable—it was an assault. We sat numbly as the lady in yellow received an immense ovation and was replaced onstage by another diva, this time in red, who delivered another showstopper at full volume.

A few rounds of the local firewater known as *urguato* revived our spirits enough to enjoy the spectacle, at least. And before long, alienation gave way to hysteria: Jamie and Michael performed impromptu on-camera endorsements for *urguato*—she as a Peking Opera star, he as a Beijing cabdriver. Soon, we wept and howled in a painful ecstasy of mockery and mustard sauce. The musical gamut had been run that day. But in between sobs of laughter, I wondered: would we ever hear this as anything but infernal caterwauling? Where was our broad base of cultural knowledge? Did Chinese music not enter into our stylistic lingua franca? We ordered another round.

The next day, while Michael continued working with the orchestra, I accompanied Jamie to Beijing University where she had been invited to give a talk about LB's music. To our delight, the lecture hall was packed. Brief interviews I held with some of the music students outside revealed a general appreciation of LB as a conductor but nothing of him as a composer. For the next hour and a half, Jamie played various CDs and videos of LB works. She talked about his uncanny ability to give symphonic expression to popular idiom, as in *West Side Story* and the *Age of Anxiety* Symphony. The students responded instinctively to his music and rewarded Jamie with a great many questions, all of which she dispatched expertly until one young man asked: "Did your father enjoy Chinese music?" Here, Jamie balked. She looked pleadingly at me but I could offer no help on this. The probable truth, she offered, was that he never crossed paths with it.

We knew, of course, that had he ever traveled to China during his life and heard Chinese music, he would surely have plumbed its mysteries and might even have fallen madly in love with it. But China never invited him to perform until, ironically, just before the Tiananmen Square massacre. Needless to say, he never went and so remained unacquainted with Chinese music all his life. This unofficial cultural embargo, sad to say, cut both ways to lasting effect. I doubt that *The Peony Pavilion*, for instance, that Peking Opera classic, appears much on Juilliard's opera syllabus.

> The students responded instinctively to his music and rewarded Jamie with a great many questions, all of which she dispatched expertly until one young man asked: "Did your father enjoy Chinese music?"

. . . .

With the exception of one of the American sopranos losing her voice at the last minute, Saturday evening's concert went extremely well. Michael's efforts had paid off. The musicians heard the music as it should be played and finally understood its beauty and charm. At intermission, the mood backstage had a new lightness to it, and musicians were smiling broadly for my camera. They had turned a tremendous corner and they knew it.

The following morning brought crisp, autumn weather to Beijing—a welcome change from the damp, smoggy soup that had choked us all week. The *Bernstein Beat* concert was scheduled for 1:00. The theatre stood at the far end of a pretty little park near the Forbidden City. An unmistakably Chinese red lacquered gate gleamed against the October sky and marked the entrance to the park. Just inside, thousands of brightly colored balloons in the form of a rainbow advertized a huge pharmaceuticals trade fair. People were arriving by the hundreds to peruse row upon row of exotic pills, creams, teas, and elixirs.

Over at the other side of the park, children were assembling for the concert, drawn magnetically by the free McDonald's Happy Meals being distributed by the shrewd music festival staff. (During the ensuing feeding frenzy, we noted that more than a few of the children were looking uncharacteristically pudgy. We had also heard that juvenile diabetes was on the rise in China.) After lunch, the children were escorted inside and treated to a magic show given by an honest-to-God regulation Ronald McDonald clown. When his tricks fell flat, he threw candy.

Meanwhile, Jamie and her translator were putting the finishing touches on the script. They had worked doggedly to convert the colloquial, American script to a Chinese equivalent. One section in particular had worried Jamie ever since she first planned to bring the show to China. At one point in the concert, the orchestra plays a frenzied, rhythmically complex excerpt from LB's *MASS*. Afterward, Jamie explains how to make sense of its asymmetrical, nine-beat bars. Each bar, she says, can be broken down into two and three-beat "rhythm packages" featuring strong and weak beats. She assigns the word "hot dog" to the two-beat package and "ham burger" to the three-beat package. Thus, one of the *MASS* bars scans as "ham burger, hot dog, hot dog, hot dog." In the States, with nine volunteer kids onstage holding colored plackards to represent the beats in the measure, this game worked brilliantly. But Chinese is a tonal language, where syllables are not stressed so much as sung. Would Chinese kids get the point? And how does one translate hamburger and hot dog, anyway?

Jamie's translator, a serene, child-friendly lady named Gao Lin, assured her that hamburgers, "hambubu," were known in China. (Confirmed.) As for hot-dogs, they go by the literal translation "re-go." Not exactly mellifluous to our ears but Gao promised that she would make every effort to stress where stress was due.

Once the concert began, it wasn't immediately clear if the script was getting through to the kids. They sat very still and correctly, and didn't laugh at the jokes. But when Jamie asked for her nine volunteers, dozens of children swarmed down the aisles to the stage and we knew they were with us. The orchestra had played the excerpt from MASS and Jamie had outlined the basic concept of dividing up the nine-beat rhythm into packages. Now they were going to play a game that would cement the idea. Four of the children held yellow plackards to represent the strong beats in the measure (Ham—, Hot -, Hot -, Hot -) and the other five held blue ones to represent the weak, inner beats (—burger, -dog, -dog, -dog.) Jamie then grouped them into the hamburger and hot-dog packages. The children looked understandably confused at first, but when the tom-tom began to play the rhythm from the piece and Gao chanted "ham bubu, re-go, re-go, re-go," along with it, their faces beamed. Later on, when Jamie invited the entire audience to shout "MAMBO!!" during the *West Side Story* "Dance at the Gym" sequence, they were so jazzed that they roared it.

They may have begun their afternoon as the objects of vulgar pandering, but now their minds were fully engaged in a serious lesson by way of serious fun: the old Bernstein family recipe. And to see them embrace LB's music on such a visceral level gratified our very souls. To their open, unindoctrinated ears, it had no extra-musical significance; it was simply music, welcome and free.

Along with the games and the lessons, the *Bernstein Beat* is a tour of LB's musical influences, from Jewish liturgy to Cuban *huapangos*. As Jamie explains at the end of her narration, the crazy salad of all these ingredients is, in a way, the musical equivalent of America itself: brazen and eclectic but with its own, distinct flavor. At the end of the day, we bid a grateful farewell to the orchestra. From their gleeful grins and their unexpectedly emotional good-byes, we dared to hope that some of the week's cross-cultural ice had melted; that maybe the flavor of America would now hold more dimension than a Big Mac; that the word—the music—would spread. As for us, we are determined to make the effort to catch *The Peony Pavilion* next time it comes to New York—followed, I hope, by a raucous feast in Chinatown.

THE Cotton Club

—AN EXCERPT FROM—

1929: A Novel of the Jazz Age

The Cotton Club was originally Jack Johnson's idea and so was the choice of Ellington as the house band. But Johnson's been muscled out by the white gangsters Owney Madden, Big Frenchy DeMange, and their bunch and now serves principally as a greeter, standing at the door in a heavy-cut suit and the British bowler he loves to affect, massive, black as basalt, his gold-capped teeth glittering in the marquee lights that shower on his shoulders like powder. The old champ's perfect for the spectacle inside. He's knocked men senseless, fixed fights, done time for illicit activities with white women. He's dangerous, damaged, debonair, and so it's a thrill for midtowners, out-of-towners, visiting firemen and their wives when Champion Jack doffs that bowler at the doorway and offers you the great, pink-palmed mitt that once crashed against the jaw of Jim Jeffries, settling the hash of the Great White Hope.

By Frederick Turner

— ENTRANCE TO THE COTTON CLUB —

Maurice Ravel has been taken into a number of high-class clubs over here, but still he's astonished that there should be so huge and glittering a display as this, right out in the open—and in the Negro quarter, too.

It's just right for the Cotton Club, because inside the door Johnson holds open for you, you get the same heady mixture of color, crime and high style. There's Big Frenchy himself in a conspicuously loud suit, sitting at a table next to Duke on the bandstand. And over there is the speakeasy owner Mexico Gomez, who once served as a machine gunner for Black Jack Pershing. And there's the gyrating dancer, Snake Hips Tucker. And Duke, too—he's part of the whole, artful package: brilliantly handsome, lacquered hair, mustache so perfect it looks like somebody drew it on his lip; French-vanilla-colored cutaway; smile as ordered and white as the piano he plays with flashy hand flourishes. And up behind him and his sharp-suited band, Sonny Greer and his spectacular pile of percussive instruments—traps, bass drum, tom-toms, chimes, wood blocks, cymbals, Chinese gongs. Owney Madden bought him these, and now every bootlegger with big American dreams wants to back a band with a drummer set up just like Sonny. And who knows? The way new clubs keep opening all over the country, there may still be room at the top with Owney and Scarface, Dutch and Bugs.

Maurice Ravel has been taken into a number of high-class clubs over here, but still he's astonished that there should be so huge and glittering a display as this, right out in the open—and in the Negro quarter, too. The place seats seven hundred on two horseshoe tiers, and everything in it has a high, uniform polish, from the greeter's gold teeth to the sound of the showers of the silver dollars flung at the feet of the waiter who sings at your table between sets, his tray balanced on palm, ceremonial napkin draped over his arm like a flag of state. The theme is jungle. Palms everywhere. Potted palms around the edges of the vast room. Palms painted on the stage curtains, on the cover of the program they hand you when Champion Jack shows you in. Also on that cover, in front of the palms, depictions of jungle men pounding out savage rhythms on tom-toms bigger than kettle drums, white-fanged mouths ecstatically agape. Savage women with ripe, bare breasts. Duke plays along with all this, and his band formerly booked as the Washingtonians is now popularly called the Jungle Band. They play Jungle Blues, Jungle Jamboree, Jungle Nights in Harlem. But what fascinates Ravel, once he's adjusted to the visual assault of the place, is how the band talks through their instruments. Even listening to Bechet in Paris hasn't prepared him for such a full-throated, communal conversation. The players laugh, cry, worry, argue, scoff, banter, gossip, explain, wonder, grieve. He hardly notices Snake Hips Tucker and the long-limbed chorus girls who are all the same light bronze color as if issued by a machine. He feels he's listening to a tribal council and tries to figure out how this effect is produced, what its essence is, and the more he listens, the more he finds it isn't the leader himself, whose playing he finds colorful and stylish but ultimately ordinary. Nor is it the drummer, high in his shining, thundering authority. Instead the heart of the band is one of the trumpet players with his vocalized style, his growls and shouts, interjections, and wa-wa's. He's where that unique sound comes from, flipping his mute back and forth so deftly he seems to the listening composer more magician or conjurer than musician. Ravel asks about him, and Bix tells him he's Bubber Miley. When Miley isn't waving that mute, producing those growls and wa-wa's, he wears a diffident, even haughty expression, eyebrows slightly lifted, as though the disparities and contradictions of his situation are nightly impressed upon him as he surveys the black waiters, black dancers, white patrons scattering their silver over the floor. Ravel wants to know more about him, whether such an extensive, dexterous use of mutes is common in jazz music, and Bix tells him that very few can use them the way Bubber does. Most of the time, he says, players use them to disguise inferior tone. Only King Oliver comes to mind as Bubber's equal. But he stops there, deciding not to go on about the King, down there years ago at Lincoln Gardens on the South Side, the place stinking of urine and spilled beer, and the King up there with the plunger on over his horn on the deep blues: on those numbers he could get down so low, so quiet you could hear the dancers' feet gliding through the dust, through the dry, burnt husks of discarded cigarettes. Instead, Bix merely asks if Ravel wants a refill of the seltzer he's drinking, and when Ravel says yes, Bix signals the waiter and orders also two more of Madden's

Number One beer—vile stuff that Herman says Capone would never sell even in his crummiest dive. Bix only shrugs, what-the-hell.

It's well after one when Ravel signals with raised brows that he's had enough, and Bix, watching for this and amazed at the old man's stamina and level of interest, springs up and asks Herman if he'll wait with Ravel while he sees about a cab. When he gets back to the booth, there's Herman talking with Big Frenchy. At a distance Big Frenchy has a kind of Teddy Bear look until you're close enough to see the merciless eyes set deep beneath Neolithic eyebrows that would meet over his crooked pug nose except that Big Frenchy in some obscure gesture of vanity shaves the intervening space; and maybe it's for the best because with the eyebrows joined there he wouldn't look merely colorful to Mort and Mabel from Minneapolis. He'd look positively frightening. So this is a cosmetic compromise, like many other things in the Cotton Club. "I made you right off," Big Frenchy's saying to Herman with Ravel still sitting in the booth, fingers poised on his thin lips. "I made you from Chi, musta been, what, two years ago." Herman nods. He remembers Big Frenchy, too, from a big gangster get-together at the Metropole, but he doesn't say so. In this world it's often best not to admit you remember a man's face. So he merely nods and when Big Frenchy asks what he's up to these days, Herman tells him he's band manager for Whiteman. "And this," he says, turning to Bix, "is Bix—he's with Whiteman, too." Big Frenchy looks down at Bix, and a slight, sardonic smile comes on his face. "Whiteman and that guy with the French name who writes his stuff—they come up here, musta been five, six nights in a row. Sat right over there," gesturing toward a table right under the bandstand on which a comedian is doing a number with a dog and a girl assistant. "Looking, listening, trying to figure out how Duke does it. Oh, I seen 'em. Did everything except take notes." Bix smiles up at Big Frenchy, open, disarming, spreading his hands slowly from his sides in wordless assent. "But you can't get down what Duke does," Big Frenchy goes on, the smile now shading into one of satisfaction. "That's stuff you and Whiteman can't heist. Can't be done." He turns back to Herman, and Bix, beginning to get anxious about the waiting Ravel and the cab idling out front, looks to Herman to somehow wind this up and sees Herman looking easy enough, standing clear of the booth, and Bix can see too that his long upper lip is quite dry under the blue glaze of its heavy beard. "How's

On the ride back down to Ravel's hotel the little Frenchman is huddled and silent, as though suddenly exhausted by the long night's dark dazzle.

---

it suit ya, this band stuff?" Big Frenchy asks. "Okay?" "Okay," Herman comes back. "Okay. Still workin' with cars, motors. Still haulin'. Long nights, short sleeps." "Yeah, well," Big Frenchy says, dubious, raising his voice through a laugh the comedian's gotten with the doggie and the girl, "you ever want to change your shoes, you found me here." The laugh begins to die. "You'd be surprised," Big Frenchy says, "good's the money is, how hard it is finding reliable people. Steady. I heard about you in Chi." Herman nods again in acknowledgment, and Big Frenchy sticks out his hand, and Herman, hesitating something less than a beat, extends his, and they meet in a clasp that regains something of its ancient signification: no weapons here. Then Herman says he appreciates the idea and Big Frenchy turns away, presenting his wide back, bulging under its suitcoat, and begins working a few tables on his way to his own table, right next to the stage, where he'll sit until closing. And then, while everything's being packed up and the mops and brooms come out he'll play whist and pinochle with Duke and the boys until breakfast is served with the sun.

On the ride back down to Ravel's hotel the little Frenchman is huddled and silent, as though suddenly exhausted by the long night's dark dazzle, and neither Bix nor Herman wants to intrude with so much as a stray word. At the hotel Bix hops out to escort Ravel to the door where a sleepy doorman, slumped inside his heavy braid coat, makes only a perfunctory gesture at his job. And then Herman watches an exchange between the composer and Bix, Ravel speaking earnestly to Bix and Bix nodding quickly, three times, and then Bix almost running back to the cab, and Herman's already told the cabbie the next stop's the Forty-Fourth Street Hotel. But then Herman finds Bix almost glaring at him in the white, flittering lights, and saying, "Herman! Hey, Herman! Let's live a little!" And Herman, looking at that now drawn, white-and-black face, feels something between a profound weariness with it all and a disgust for it, too, and says, "Aw, Christ, Bix, why not let it alone."

Little Waltz

by

Adam Zagajewski

Translated by Clare Cavanagh

The days are so vivid, so bright

that even the slim, sparse palms

are covered in the white dust of neglect.

Serpents in the vineyards slither softly,

but the evening sea grows dark and,

suspended overhead like punctuation

in the highest script, the seagulls barely stir.

A drop of wine's inscribed upon your lips.

The limestone hills slowly melt

on the horizon and a star appears.

At night on the square an orchestra of sailors

dressed in spotless white

plays a little waltz by Shostakovich; small children

cry as if they'd guessed

what the merry music's really saying.

We've been locked in the world's box,

love sets us free, time kills us.

bong bong bong bong (Silence)

SAMPLING UTOPIAN (NON) MUSIC IN TOKYO

BY DAVID GRUBBS

when I return from an early dinner at the conveyor-belt sushi restaurant, the crowd outside the Kichijoji Star Pine's Café circles halfway around the block. The Sunday evening concert is divided into two sets. The first consists of solo performances by four Japanese musicians, two Parisians, and one American; the second, a half-dozen small improvising groups drawn from the pool of seven players.

The first performer is a Japanese woman in her late twenties, the only woman on the bill. Her Philip K. Dickian instrument is the sampler without memory, and she often collaborates with someone who plays the "no-input mixing board"—so-called, even though the board's output is connected to its input, thus completing a feedback loop. A similar query could be made about calling her instrument the sampler without memory. As source material, she uses the sampler's sine-wave test tones—its earliest and evidently only remaining memories.

Think of Bartleby's flutelike voice.

Transpose that sound five or more octaves upward, and leave your pets at home. The manipulation of the sine-wave source material generally takes one of two forms: either a gentle, dotlike tattoo (Morse) or a beating caused by superimposing two or more pitches that differ by only a few cents (moiré). In Elem Klimov's 1985 film *Come and See*, a boy who's defied his family to join the Soviet army during the Second World War is partially deafened by an explosion. What I remember most vividly about the film is the radical removal after the explosion of low- and mid-frequency sounds, the filtering of the soundtrack in an attempt to approximate hearing damage. That's one way of describing this performance. You find yourself wondering why all the sound is trapped way up there in a high-frequency whine. Have you suddenly become unable to hear below seventeen thousand cycles per second? At the beginning of the set, before it becomes apparent that no wild gestures are in the offing, the sound seems poised to make a qualitative change, the change from liquid to gas. Are we waiting for that piercing squall to be ratcheted beyond audibility and into some approximation of silence?

She plays for eight or ten minutes or however long has been allotted. Very little changes in that length of time. I wish I could describe it as an ear cleanser, but it feels more like it's wrecking my hearingor making me imagine that my hearing is wrecked. A good choice for an opener, certainly. Eight or ten minutes is a decent length for this, although relations of scale between the rippling and beating and the duration of the performance are, to say the least, obscure.

I like the experience, and that includes its cessation. How could anyone not enjoy the subsequent silence? The silence gives way to the sound of two hundred people clapping. The crowd had been remarkably quiet—no audible conversations, very little physical movement. I, on the other hand, am more accustomed to the wars that are waged between quieter performers and louder bar patrons. I have been both. In the former role, I have looked out from the stage and fantasized about a soundproof, Plexiglas curtain that could come ringing down to separate performance area and bar. Or a button to be installed onstage, perhaps a theatrically large, inevitably red panic button resorted to à la *The Gong Show*.

No such prop is needed at the Star Pine's Café. A friend is virtually set upon by the crowd for shattering the stillness with a flash photo. For much of the first set I stand in the balcony behind an immaculately groomed professional couple in their late thirties who share a small, round table and a bottle of red wine. They also share silent, meaningful looks whenever any meaningful event interrupts the stillness or the silence that have in the last two years become characteristic of many Tokyo-based improvisers.

Next up is a spectacularly rumpled guitarist—snaggletoothed, with an almost shapeless black canvas hat. A mid-sixties Guild hollowbody guitar with sunburst finish advertises Music and contrasts with the sampler without memory, which resembles a fax machine. The last time I saw this guitarist was in Chicago three years ago; someone's South Michigan Avenue loft space had been temporarily converted into a recording studio, and two days of round-the-clock sessions paired this guy with anyone who dropped by to play. (An endearing mem-

ory of Chicago.) At that time he favored a solid-body guitar and bent single notes in a rigorously pared down, slow-motion style that sometimes did and sometimes didn't feel like blues music. Between takes he slowly and aimlessly rolled around the

> ## Transpose that sound five or more octaves upward, and leave your pets at home.

loft on a skateboard slugging Jim Beam. He was then wearing a beat-up fedora rather than the beat-up canvas hat.

Three years later, and his blues are gone. Or rather the blues idiom in his playing. Oh, but the amp buzz and the sound of a not particularly well grounded electric guitar can be sad and blue. Time soundlessly ticks into his eight to ten minutes. I'm accustomed to seeing avant-garde musicians "prepare" their instruments with decisive, lightning-fast gestures. Personal fan, check. Screwdriver, check. Further implements, more toys. The guitar player takes his own sweet time, much as the fastest runner in baseball becomes the slowest walker on earth after beating out a suicide squeeze. Rumpled guitarist weaves a discarded string through the strung six, presumably creating a delicate mute that accentuates chosen harmonics. I say "presumably," because all we hear is the distant sound of amp buzz. Three alligator clips are produced and carefully clamped onto the strings. A percussion mallet is selected and rejected. A second mallet is selected, this one a blue rubber ball at the end of a wooden rod. Unexpectedly, he strikes the body of the instrument in three different spots—one two three, bong bong bong—three similar sounds issuing from three dissimilar attacks. Very suave!

> The crowd takes equal pleasure in the silence that yields to sound and the sound that shades into silence.

The professional couple share a smile over their bottle of wine.

Having executed this unexpected fluorescence, the triple bloom-burst that was bong bong bong, the guitarist now begins to undo his preparations. Perhaps he makes slightly more noise in disassembling than in assembling, I don't recall. Other events probably occur. The crowd takes equal pleasure in the silence that yields to sound and the sound that shades into silence. There's an element of theater in the performance, but different from that of the avant-blues vagabond glimpsed in Chicago three years earlier. Again, eight or ten minutes. Glory be. In his case the arc of the performance, the gestures made, do seem particularly appropriate for their duration. When the end is signaled—and that's the way it happens—the Star Pine's Café meets silence with volume. In spades.

Nice people. Utopian Sunday.

• • •

Two nights prior, I had caught the final set of an evening of improvised music at Tokyo's Uplink. There were eight musicians, including three of the four Japanese players who performed at the Star Pine's event. The pool was rounded out by an American, a German, and three Austrians.

I run into the American on my way in. He tells me that the first set had been devoted to smaller groups, but that the last will feature everyone playing together.

"But, you know, not everyone playing together."

How would I know? How does he know?

I understand this as indicative of a trend in improvised music toward long gaps of relative inactivity clustered at the cusp of silence. This tendency strikes me as a reaction to the extended palette of much recent electronic and electroacoustic music, not to mention the often bewildering speed and complexity with which it hurtles toward or past the listener.

The final set at Uplink begins with nobody making a sound. For several minutes. From the performers, lots of conspicuous not looking at one another.

Silence, solo, duo, trio, duo, solo, silence.

Lots of not playing together.

The ambient sounds of the venue aren't so grand. No rhythms of rain and roof. (Derek Bailey's *Music and Dance* and Phil Durant, Thomas Lehn, and Radu Malfatti's *dach* are both records that prominently feature this incursion of nature.) Some pleasure is to be had in the smallness of the sound, in the underscoring of the distance—small as the space is—between sounding body and listener. Overwhelmingly the performance dra-matizes restraint. Ugh. The whole thing seems so damn coercive at the level of the individual participant.

Does anyone think that the category of silence would have been similarly evocative had John Cage not selected the word for the title of his first and most influential collection of writings? What do these performances have to do with John Cage's famous "silent" piece, *4' 33"*? Or with its reprise, *0' 00" (4' 33" No. 2)*? The latter was first performed in Tokyo in 1962, and its score is as follows: "In a situation provided with maximum amplification (no feedback), perform a disciplined action." The vogue for very quiet, verging on silent improvised music not only has little to do with Cage's work—it seems predicated on forgetting Cage. Forgetting the Cage, that is, who added the qualification that the disciplined action in *0' 00"* should not be repeated in subsequent performances.

The restraint of the solo performers at the Star Pine's, in contrast to the Uplink show, came across as quixotic, mischievous, slightly sad-clownish, and above all volitional. At any point a performer could have changed course and paddled as loudly and erratically as possible in the opposite direction. I imagine those performers as having moments of true disbelief in the audience's response—waiting for someone to sneeze, waiting to wake up, waiting for something unpredicted, waiting for someone to call the whole thing off.

My Guitar

TRADING PEN FOR PIC AT AGE THIRTY-EIGHT

BY DARCEY STEINKE

By the end of last summer my girl-friends and I had repeated our worries, our mostly mundane longings for love, so many times that they were becoming refrains, like in rock-and-roll songs. My friend Biz Mitchell, recognizing the crisis for what it was, suggested we start a band. We were sitting at a table in Double Happiness on Mott Street and I can remember the flickering candle illuminating her face as she tried to convince me. I'd played the flute in elementary school, mostly unsuccessfully. My Greek teacher yelled at me every time I fell off rhythm or dropped notes.

The next day I still couldn't believe I was going to buy a guitar. I was thirty-eight and since I'd left my husband, I had little money to spare. The thing would sit in my closet and collect dust. I constructed excuses: my credit card was maxed out, there wasn't enough money in my checking, I was afraid of getting electrocuted. But Biz was waiting for me outside Sam Ash and once inside we were mesmerized by the racks of guitars. They looked like the shells of exotic sea animals. Rocker boys scattered around the store played well-traveled riffs. A salesman, sporting a goatee, approached us, asked if we wanted a demonstration. We nodded as he sat on a stool and took down first a brown-and-cream sunburst model that Biz admired. He said it was similar to Paul McCartney's bass. Next I pointed to a slender burgundy guitar which he told us was like Pete Townsend's. This one had a harsh metallic twang that made my heart jump. We settled on these two Gibson Epiphones. We also bought practice amps and carrying cases. But even after we loaded our new equipment into a cab and I dropped Biz off at her apartment on Nassau Street down near the World Trade towers, I felt silly—like I'd bought toy angel wings in a childish effort to fly.

That night, after I put my daughter to bed, I took out the practice book and tried to make my fingers form the first open chords. My hand, while resistant, made the A, the C, the D. But when I got to the F, a chord that requires both precision and Herculean finger strength, I despaired. I needed a teacher and I found one later that week in John Aiellio, formerly one of my students at the New School. My first

lesson was tense. I'm not so good at being bad at things and I was ashamed of how little I knew. But John is an extremely sensitive teacher. He understands that good instruction is as much about a you-can-do-it energy transfer as it is giving helpful hints. I have much to learn in all aspects of my life but it's not usually so painfully obvious as when I try to settle my fingers on the frets of my guitar.

In my high school, in Roanoke, only the boys owned electric guitars. It was as overwhelmingly a masculine endeavor as playing football. While for a brief period I borrowed an acoustic, it was only to try and play Joni Mitchell folk songs. Mitchell's alternate tunings and glass slide were way beyond me and the only music I ever learned was the melody for "A Time for Us," the theme song to Zeffirelli's film *Romeo and Juliet*. Chords seemed almost impossible and without the greater goal of starting a band I quickly gave up.

Still, the do-it-yourself glamour of rock drew me one rainy afternoon to the basement of the Baptist church behind my house where a band was playing Aerosmith covers. The lead singer, his blond hair cut in a shag, wore velvet pants and a long scarf around his neck. At the end of every song he did a handstand! The guitar player, a chubby boy, was utterly without appeal until he leaned into a riff and shut his eyes, his acne-covered face transfigured as the strap of his denim overalls unhooked and dangled down by his side.

After eight weeks of practicing on our own, our band begins to come together at a rehearsal studio in midtown Manhattan. Besides Biz and I, my cousin Rene Steinke plays keyboards and Natalie Standiford is on bass. Hawes Bostic, our drummer, comes to us a month later. In that first session we attempt David Bowie's "Five Years" and sing "She Said, She Said" by the Beatles a cappella. Biz, our most productive songwriter, previews an original called "Keep Still." Jamming is invigorating but I still feel like a fraud. We can barely manage the basic chord progressions. We are like hopeful little girls.

Original songs, we've been told, are easier to play than covers. I compose a song on the train to Sarah Lawrence, where I'm teaching, writing the lyrics like a teenager in my notebook. After class, on the train home, I figure out a melody, and in Grand Central, so I won't forget the cadence, I call my own answering machine and sing the song into the receiver.

It's called "Lefty" and it's about my frustration with my boyfriend's repressive politics. Once I have a draft of the song I play it nearly every hour. I can't stop. I'm reminded of how in college I'd jump out

of bed at night, turn on my desk lamp, and read the story I'd just written. It's the same with my new song. I love my new song, and I love my guitar.

My guitar is my favorite material object. It's better looking than my computer. It has a sumptuous body and quivering strings. I now understand Picasso's "Blue Guitar," how the instrument is not just a symbol for the body, it is the body. Transubstantiation is at work. I also love myself holding my guitar. I go at least twice a day and stand in front of the full-length mirror in my bathroom and try out different rock-star expressions. When I do this I think of my hero David Bowie, but I also am my hero David Bowie. The identification is so close it leads to identity confusion. I love the sheen of the red varnish on the guitar and I love my purple picks. I love the D and the G above all other chords. When I am in a particularly sensitive mood, a single D chord coming out of my little practice amp gives me goose bumps.

By the time my birthday rolls around in April the band has eight originals and a gig booked at the Parkside Lounge in the East Village. Instead of the usual writerly presents, books, fountain pens, blank journals, I receive a killer metal-studded guitar strap, a leather belt with a huge rhinestone buckle, and a red T-back tank top. My

Marxist boyfriend is gone, and while I miss the delicacy of his long, thin body, I don't miss how he monopolized my guitar, showing off whenever he slept over with his fancy fingerwork. When I'd see him going into that guitar-boy stupor I'd remember what Kurt Cobain told me when I interviewed him for *Spin*. It's like some Masonic cult the way men have monopolized the guitar. Kurt is another one of my guitar gods. I think of his thin frame and filthy hair and how in his presence you felt the rock-and-roll godhead shining through.

Kurt hovers around me as I practice and I have a dream he asks me to join his band. Everybody has to play kazoo, he tells me. He plays the toy xylophone. The same multicolored Fisher-Price model I cherished as a kid. Yes, I want to join! Of course! But every time I try to copy down his heavenly address my fingers won't let me form the letters and finally he evaporates, leaving me with the same sense of frustration I have when I can't make my fingers stay on the frets. I'm always twilling the high E. I'm always messing up. I can never hook into the groove.

As a little girl I wanted to stick my fingers into an electrical socket. Of course I'd been warned repeatedly against this, but I'd eye the beige plastic outlet with the two silver screws longingly. I was amazed at the force that came

out of the little slits; like magic it animated the blades on the blender, put a picture up on my television screen, and made the vacuum roar. A few times I stuck a paper clip into the holes and sparks flew out, but it wasn't until I plugged my guitar into the amp and my amp into the wall that I felt the wonder and power of electricity and through that force the splendor of the modern world. Still there is a great distance between what I can do and what I long to do. I want to harness the power of the planets, gather the static of the universe, bring into confluence the rhythmic patterns of heartbeats, the seasons, sirens, chrysanthemum petals falling, chain saws, sleet, baby talk, radio waves, love, the subway, thinking. But of course I can't.

On the afternoon before our first gig I play along with our practice tape ten times. We've taken the name Ruffian from the champion filly who ran in the late seventies. We even have a ballad about our little-girl selves watching Ruffian break down on national television. At the Parkside there is a silver curtain in back of the stage made of tinsel, but the platform is so small we can hardly move. Oddly, I'm not that nervous, I have my best friends around me and though on one song we slide off the rhythm, and on another I sing the wrong words, I feel okay. Playing live is oddly anticlimactic, not the ultimate experience I'd anticipated. Not unlike writing, the process of composing and practicing is more satisfying than performing. I'm reminded of dance recitals in grade school, how I only remembered a few sensations, the stage lights in my eyes, the silhouetted bodies in the audience, and then nothing. The middle of our Ruffian show is similarly blurry, and it's not until the last song, a cover of Jonathan Richman's "She Cracked," that I discover the main difference between giving a reading at KGB Bar and playing in my band. Endorphins. You can almost see them opening up like flowers in people's eyes.

Midsummer I take Abbie, my daughter, to a cabin in the Blue Ridge Mountains. Every night, after I put her to bed, I plug in my guitar. It's a tremendous comfort to do scales, work on "Brown Sugar," "Young Americans," and the new Ruffian songs, which are all more rhythmically complex than the earlier batch. The notes each express to my ear the fragility of humanity. Human sorrow and ambivalence seem to be what the guitar was meant to express. I practice for an hour, working myself into that rare space, similar to when Abbie was a baby and my repeated nursing, bathing, and soothing

> Human sorrow and ambivalence seem to be what the guitar was meant to express.

led us into eternal time, into a holy patch as palpable to me as a weather front.

As I finish writing this in late September, New York City is a changed landscape, emotionally as well as geographically. Biz's apartment on Nassau Street is covered with the dust of the incinerated. Biz escaped her neighborhood with clothes pulled over her pajamas. Ruffian is safe but shaken. We're ambivalent about our usual Sunday-night rehearsal. We decide to go ahead, though not at our usual space on Twenty-Sixth Street, but rather at a small studio in Brooklyn.

We run through our set without talking between songs. Our continuous expression of shock has brought on another verbal dead end. We play with a combination of passionate intensity and limpness that has characterized my mood since the attack. I perform mostly badly, missing notes and coming in wrong. But when I finally do settle into the groove I feel so grateful to be inside this room with the beer-stained carpet and the dirty ashtrays. I feel privileged I can merge, no matter how incompetently or momentarily, into the world's vaster rhythms. I feel intensely thankful to be playing guitar.

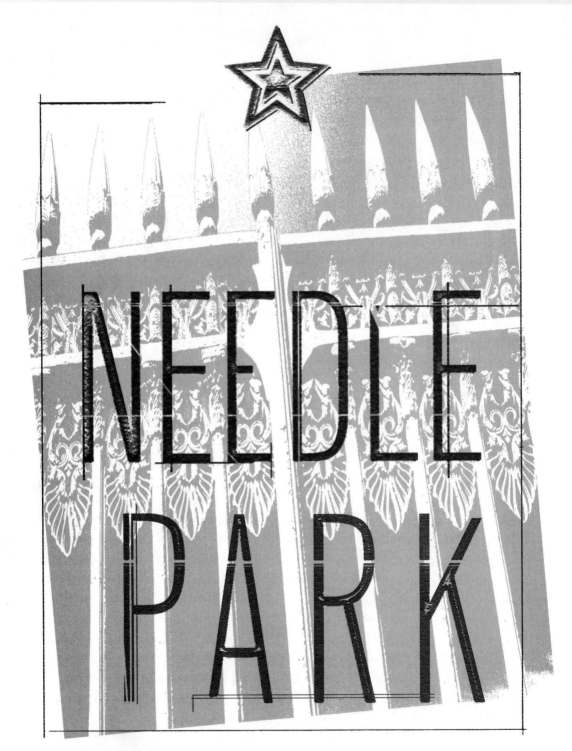

NEEDLE PARK

BY DAVID RYAN

or months I spent the evenings watching men and women carry on about their business behind apartment windows. I was the judge. My window overlooked dozens of windows set into the back sides of the facing tenements and brownstones.

The scenes afforded a great deal of variety, if of a bland type. I eventually chose a certain woman who tried on blouses all night in front of a mirror. Or I guessed it was a mirror, given the intent way she stared ahead, and by how deliberate it seemed when she cupped her figure in the light with the flattened palms of her hands.

Deliberate because how could she deny the existence of the courtyard, all those windows, the blindless barrier of glass and open distance between the two of us. Because of this distance, I couldn't tell what she looked like, except that her figure was young and that she appeared both sickly and healthy, the way people who work in the lower levels of offices tend to look. Or perhaps she was a saleswoman at a department store. She may have used a gym regularly, to compensate. She seemed manufactured into some alien mass of padded skin and sprayed hair, blemishes vaguely well concealed. She didn't seem real, but it was the best I could do.

She tried on her wardrobe almost every night in plain view. I had trouble understanding how the clothes were different from one costume change to the next. She kept leaving the bathroom door open. Her television never turned off. Soon I grew bored, switched my lights on, then off. Then I'd leave them on again, sitting on my bed naked, trying to make the guilt of it more interesting.

One night another man entered her apartment—a new acquaintance, perhaps, as I'd never seen him until then—and ended the contract between us by taping a sheet over the window. As he pulled the cloth across the glass he looked over the courtyard in my direction, then extended the middle finger of his hand. Later, he put up blinds. I never saw her again, except slivered.

Once, in Zurich, I wandered into a nightclub alone, intending to meet a few friends, and quickly realized that I had entered the wrong bar, that I was the only one there who wasn't a transvestite. No one had to tell me I wasn't welcome. I could see it in the way I became a shadow in the center of the room, and so I quietly left. The following evening I had the feeling that my hands and feet were made of an even more foreign substance than they probably were, and would crumble if touched just so by the right person. I itched all over, deep into my muscles (this is how lonely I was), and realized how incrementally I was decomposing as I vomited in installments the heroin a friend and I had procured in Needle Park. There were dozens of dealers in this park. Of them all, we chose someone who in no way resembled the person whom I would someday become.

Later that night I had dreams that a large man held a pillow over my face, his belly pressed against my back, throbbing. It seemed far too easy for him to do, under the abraded circumstances. Some kind of spring kept disgorging, a pellet gun going off into my ear, blasting out dots of my brain, sending glowing holes into the backs of my eyes.

I was with a particular crowd at this time. I was a musician. By then we'd become like greyhounds chasing a rabbit, only to discover the flesh and blood was in fact tin and machine oil. It was not uncommon to see a body lying around and to question whether or not it needed a doctor and, if so, what was the number for 911 here, and if this number were discovered, who exactly would do the talking, who exactly was in any condition to do the talking.

The dealer we chose at the park in Zurich had special braces for her arms and legs. It was moving, how pathetic and graceful she was, clutching the aluminum poles that extended from her own insuffi-ciencies. She didn't approach us, but instead moved in a kind of refined lunge. Everything she did was as if she didn't know how to do it or as if she kept rein-venting before us how she'd been intro-duced to the world. I found this beautiful. She spoke severe English to us and we thanked her. At our feet, the used needles, thousands, applauded as we walked over them. Leaving the park we passed couples who sat on the banks of the canal and injected heroin into the backs of each other's hands. I thought, Who am I to be here, watching this like a voyeur?

I was the drummer. I had long before bound myself to the punctuation of the drum; to it alone I was loyal during ado-lescence, to the precise kiss of the stick against the tightened skin, the slight gasp of a wire brush as it passed over the head of the drum. This is all I had in mind: kiss-ing and rubbing and somehow drawing out the blush from things. I became sin-gle-minded in my purpose. And when I couldn't be with my drums I beat the sticks into my body, so that around my knees a bruised enthusiasm for their touch pooled over the skin. Joining a band was simply a pretext, or so I thought, once I became an adult. It was a day job to me.

In America, southern mothers would bring their adolescent daughters to our performances and display them in a kind of openly sacrificial gesture. These south-ern mothers arrived in packs. You want to talk about desire? Southern mothers, their thin shoulders, wizened hips, creased and tarted faces, and in front of them, the skinny promises of their own fading youth. Flesh and bone and shel-lacked hair, their suggestiveness was intended in the youthful finery, in their children's gangly posture, in how it had been arranged before us, lacquered nails burrowing into the shoulders of their younger incarnations, knuckled and lotioned hands presenting the hope of their failed past to us.

I had once been a fan myself. For example, in 1979: the ballroom's ceiling moved, rigged so that a night sky punc-tured with constellations passed over-head. I was thirteen at the time. The band opened with "So You Want to Be a Rock 'N' Roll Star." I believed the vocalist, her every word. Moreover I was lulled into something, into faith, by the single stroke roll at the end of the song. It seemed to set plainly before me every sound I would need in my lifetime. The drummer changed me.

Because when the drums enter you they enter you as all the things you could never say. None of those words have been invented. You blame lyrics for encourag-ing suicides, assassins, mass murderers. So do lovers shape themselves out of the songs sung into them. So do the hopeless shape hope from the rhythms battered into them.

In my own adolescence I learned to superimpose threes over the span of time that twos normally filled, then I tried fives and sevens and nines over fours, over threes, over twos…. It was magic I wanted, not the suggestion of some tawdry used-up flesh. I knew that in more capable hands the polyrhythms could get others to walk over fire, drive blades into their hearts without drawing blood. I wanted someone to believe me this badly.

Once our tour manager jumped out of the window of a pension we were staying at, in Ghent. He fell four flights onto a perfectly still asphalt parking lot and the growing outline of his blood pooled around him. He had been sleepwalking. He lived. We made sure before we left him there, waited until he told us why. He later admitted that halfway along the descent he woke from a dream in which he was the size of a doll, in which everything around him had been proportionately small and harmless. The leap appeared to be no more than a hop. He felt a shift in his surroundings: from the trick of sleep to a vague and simple annoyance. How rude this approaching surface! He could have slept

in! He watched the asphalt rise and grow onto him.

We left him at a Belgian intensive-care unit, alone. We had to make it to London the following day. The bass player drove because he was dyslexic and we thought he might be better equipped to handle London traffic.

What I recall of touring America mostly is the same hotel we'd left a dozen hours ago, the same hotel staff, even, magically reappearing, perhaps a little surlier now, the room already weary from us, the bed cover smelling of someone else's after-shaved neck. Some girl in a parking lot extends two yellow smiley-faced tabs of acid and says, You might want to take both hits because this shit is weak and no doubt you're used to stronger, *you're a rock-and-roll star*. And something about the deadened way she says the last bit, for just a moment, sounds as if you'd cheated her badly in some past you can't quite remember.

So our singer takes the two tabs right there, right after she says this, in much the same manner that our bass player would smash car windows for a bottle of scrips, dry-swallow what was there, then read the label. The acid girl walks away. Which is fine by singer. He's never had much of an attraction to acid girls in loose cotton love sheets, with love and peace and all that hippie costumery tie-dyed around their skinny rich bodies. A couple of hours later he embarks on a nervous breakdown that will last for weeks, while we tour from town to town. It is a nightmare, but it doesn't cross anyone's mind that the tour should end, because he can still sing at night. Singer no longer speaks, no longer responds to his real name.

Now he can sing at night, for all the reasons this story would like to tell you, but during the day he communicates only by writing out fragments of his thoughts with a permanent marker on the exposed peach of his arms and feet and neck and beautiful face, which over time ripen to pure black from the ink, a kind of medical smell coming off of him. At hotel check-ins the businesspeople look at us like we're all crazy. They aren't so far off. In a band everything is contagious.

Maybe he'd sung the wrong lyric into that acid girl. I don't know. It's all foggy, people's intentions, what they want to happen to you, how they want you to love them and how they want you to die, the potency of their hatred, and who they'll tell about it late at night when they're so fucked up or otherwise broken down and unfettered that their conscience crawls out from beneath a cipher.

After a show one night the soundman and I were wandering around New

Orleans. A girl came up and asked if *we were the guys looking for the Ecstasy.* We said yes, though we had no idea who those guys really were. But the thought of ever saying the word no is incomprehensible, even if you have to lie to avoid saying it. She had no idea we were with a band. I found this refreshing by then, as we had become knowable. I found her refreshing even if I had to admit she looked like every stereotype of a white girl, even if she conjured only thoughts of mosquito repellent and egg salad and mile after mile of strip malls and restaurants with the name King in them.

Her name was Panda. We took her drugs eagerly and then she drove us around New Orleans and its suburbs. She proudly told us she was the personal assistant to David Duke, the young Republican Senate hopeful and former Ku Klux Klansman.

He's a sweetheart, she said. And I'm his biggest fan.

The soundman and I felt like agreeing. Why not? Dots of light had begun to burn thick flashbulb-white bands over the view outside the car windows, smearing hard shapes into soft shapes wherever we looked. Gentle bees had started to tickle inside us the part of the viscera where enthusiasm is excreted. At the backs of our eyes and running along the lining of our brains it felt as if, after too long a taunt, we were finally allowed to come. We would agree to anything. We had love in our hearts. What great joy to be found in the knowledge that Panda had never heard of our band.

AT NIGHT, THE SCREAMING CRAWLED AROUND IN MY DREAMS, NEVER LETTING ME FORGET.

Even in my euphoria I could tell we had entered a bad neighborhood. Headlights came at us, two bright snowballs in the window, and then filled us with their light. The other car was driving on the wrong side of the road. Or maybe we were. Panda swerved onto a tall median strip. Sparks shot out from under the car and flew up outside our window; it sounded like old people coughing, as the car found itself some fulcrum on which to tip and sway eventually in profound silence. The two tires on the left side had blown out. The front wheel sat crooked at an impossibly crippled slant. In my state of omniscience I knew this wasn't a neighborhood for a white girl named Panda. The other car had driven right past us.

Shit, Panda said. It became the only word in her vocabulary.

The only word in mine was *more*. It felt great to be alive. Nothing mattered.

Soundman said, Look—and I saw an old taxi coming down the street. He jumped out of the backseat. I followed him and I'll admit it crossed my mind that Death might be driving that cab, which only made it more alluring. We left Panda on the median with her wreck. We didn't say goodbye.

My first night ever in Europe was spent in Zurich, though this was years before I discovered Needle Park. Imagine my excitement. Two pretty girls entered the venue wearing linen skirts and clean blouses. They looked very Swiss, but what did I know? I had never before been to this world. I mistook the clarity of their eyes and the propriety, a certain refinement, with which they carried their lithe bodies to be beauty, and in a sense it was. They both vomited on themselves right there, on their blouses and their skirts, pretty faces flushed and blanched white. They paused, then continued walking, as if nothing had occurred.

That night as with every night to follow I came home with a ringing in my ears. Over time it grew into a sound like screaming. It was only tinnitus, but it became so loud that it soon contained all the roaring applause of our actual performances. As if to remind me of my successes. Because everyone knows, you always deserve what you get. And as I lay in bed the screaming continued into my sleep, no matter what I would ingest at night, the screaming crawled around in my dreams, never letting me forget the tag, the query of that famous lyric: *Do know who you are, you're a rock-and-roll star.*

Where the Kaluli Live

===== *by* =====

Eliot Weinberger

In the thick forest where the Kaluli live, at the base of Mt. Bosavi in Papua New Guinea, it's hard to see far and space is mapped by sound:

kege kege kege
an orange-faced grackle

gubogubo gubogubo
a black sicklebird

ee-yehhhh-u
the ornate fruitdove

susulubee susulubee
the superb fruitdove

so-gaaaa gya gya gya
a rufous-bellied kookaburra

wek-woo wek-woo wek-woo
the giant cuckoodove at the top of
the waterfall *gulugulugulu*
splashing in the small pools below
kubu   kubu   kubu   kubu

bawbawbawbawbaw hornbills are flapping

                             teebo-teebo teebo-teebo
                             a crested pitohui

Hehhh a sick person wheezes

                 sawlawlawbeh sawlawlawbeh
                 the trilling kingfisher

haw-gooooo the wind goes through the forest
and a dried leaf drops *dehgeh!* from a breadfruit tree

        ehhhhh the drone of the cicadas
        deh   deh   deh deh   deh
        the sucking of the bats eating fruit

                      gehlehleh gehlehleh
                      a hooded butcherbird

godó   *godó*   *godó*   the axe hits the tree
       goooooo the tree falls through the air and
               gaw! it crashes on the ground

         sehleh sehleh knives are being sharpened on a stone
         teketeketeke the anthropologist's typewriter
         and *behdehbehdehbehdeh* his Honda generator

ti   ti   titi   ti   ti   water drips after a rainstorm

and pours out

gugu   gugu   gugu   gugu   gugu

from the bamboo tubes on the roof of the longhouse

The Kaluli language is called Bosavi—named for the mountain, the col-lapsed cone of a dead volcano—and some of the birds speak it. The black-breasted woodswallow calls *bas-bas bas-bas*, "brother in law," to the uniform swiftlet, meaning that it's time to share food. The black-throated warbler says *seeyo-gogo-bayo seyo-gogo-bayo*, "I'm staying right here." The chanting scrubwren chants *kaloo-yabe kaloo-yabe*, "someone is coming." The brown oriole, who is always female, has a foul mouth and insults the men passing by: *koo-halaideh koo-halaideh*, "what a hard cock." The large-tailed nightbird says, *noo-day-oo noo-day-oo*, "grandmother bring firewood." The friarbird calls *dowo newo*, "father! mother!" for once some children were killed by an enemy and the friarbird took their voices.

A Kaluli lives in two worlds: the visible world of people and the world of their reflec-tions, where people live as wild pigs or cassowaries on the slopes of Mt. Bosavi. When a person dies, the reflection also disappears, and turns into a bird in the visible world. Birds see each other as people, and their calls are people talking to one other. The passage of life is from infant to bird.

Human songs are bird songs, and the words of a song are called "bird sound words." They are "turned-over words," words that are comprehensible but unlike anything in the spoken language, words that have a meaning underneath, on the other side. All the metaphors are based on birds, trees, lands, and waters. The songs are in the first person; the singer is alone after the death of a family member or is traveling away from home. They describe a journey, each place-name bringing up nostalgic associations, for a tree is a home, a garden is food, a bird is a person, and life is a map and a song a path through it.

A great singer has a voice like a pink-spotted fruitdove or an orange-bellied fruitdove. The singer is a bird at the top of a waterfall, and the structure of a song is a waterfall. Songs that are poorly done have too much ledge before the water drops, or too much splashing, or they linger too long in the pool before moving on. A successful song is like water rushing over the rocks and is one in which the water keeps flowing far beyond where one can see.

In the old days, twenty years ago, before the airstrips and the missionaries and the oil drillers and the gold panners and the government officials, when the longhouses were lined with enemy skulls on pikes, the most important event was a ceremony of singing, the *gisalo*.

Each village lived in a single longhouse, and the longhouses were hours apart. Once or twice a year, a village would invite another to come sing. As night fell, the visitors arrived in a double line, carrying torches, and climbed the stairs into the suddenly silent longhouse of their hosts. Stretching the entire length of the interior, the two rows, after long moments of expectation, hissed loudly *sssss*, like a tire deflating, and abruptly sat down, revealing four singers, each identically and splendidly arrayed as birds, face and body painted red, eyes outlined in a black and white painted mask, bird of paradise feathers sprouting from armbands, head in an aureole of black cassowary feathers with a single weighted and bobbing white feather in the middle, and a cascade of yellow palm leaf streamers arching from the waist up to the shoulders and down to the floor.

Three of the singers sat, and the first began at one end of the longhouse, singing softly, staring at the floor, oblivious to the crowd, bouncing slightly with knees bent in the manner of a giant cuckoodove, accompanied by the monotonous and trance-inducing rattle of a string of mussel shells stretching from his hand to the floor. Moving slowly down the length of the longhouse, his song became louder and more intense as he sang of places familiar to his hosts and the sad events associated with those streams and trees and birds and fields. The hosts wept at the songs, and when their weeping became too unbearable, someone would grab a torch and shove it into the singer's chest or shoulder. Deep in the isolation of his song, the singer continued, unresponsive as he was burned again and again, until his song ended and another singer began, building the crescendos that would lead to his own burning.

The songs lasted until dawn, and the success of the evening was remembered in its retellings by how much the hosts were made to weep and how much the singing guests were burned. The last one occurred in 1984.

In the Bosavi language, the word for "tomorrow" is the same as the word for "yesterday." The word no longer applies to Kaluli society, but the same birds who were once Kaluli

ee-yehhhh-u

eē-yehhh-u

susulubee   susulubee   susulubee

are still in the trees. ▮

Two Poems

—— *by* ——

Zoë Anglesey

Letter to Ivie

Pleasing to behold, opal satin *à plomb* and matching pumps.
You stand erect, shoulders parallel to the horizon like a level
with its telling bubble. Pride and grace require precision.

Duke's painterly colors illume the music, his monochromatic eye
the stage, don't you think? A white dress, he said, to gleam
in the galaxy of chic tuxedos or a moon among Sonny Greer's

constellation of drums, mother-of-pearl and silver-trimmed.
Nightly you wore this floor-length uniform and back in L.A., shirt-
waists to run the Chicken Shack and hotel welcome to the band.

Know instead of scratchy wools and taffetas, Emily fostered splendor
in her garden and marmalades. For Mr. Higginson, she chose
a blue shawl. Her housedress of yesterday boiled in a tub of bed-

clothes and linens, went to a washboard and rinses before given

to the cleanest breezes. Seven years a nurse as her mother lay,

I thank her white dresses for her poems, economy to work

in the day to save the night. Ivie, I admire your alabaster gowns

for the songs they dressed: "It Don't Mean a Thing If It Ain't Got

That Swing . . . just keep that rhythm, give it everything. . . ."

Emily heard the bell toll on the common for the Civil War dead—

her schoolmates. Ivie, though FDR named the Black Cabinet

and WPA good for jobs, from trees, twenty more were hung.

Blind Lemon Jefferson sank frozen in a Windy City snowdrift.

Triflin' men stirred "Troubled Waters," above-it-all gossips played

the blame 'bout one of the devil's daughters. Ivie, you stayed

the wiser. Emily too. If people go 'round scandalizin' names,

no mind, the art lasts longer. I still hear azure horns enunciate

your words. And all those years, remember, lovers danced.

Louis Armstrong and Consequences

According to the Campus Crier, *Louis Armstrong,*

plus the All-Stars, a six-piece touring band, performed

on January 16, 1962, in Nicholson Pavilion [Central Washington

University, Ellensburg, Washington].

The band was rushed and the student reporter had

difficulty completing an interview. Therefore, there was

no review or pictures. Nothing appeared in the town paper.

I learned from Neruda, fish always know how to dress for the sea.

When my hubby-to-be asked me why the leopard skin and black,

he got a look that said You don't understand, the map charts

a world bigger than this rodeo town.

That's about the time I saw Jackie Kennedy in those bateau

suits and Marilyn Monroe keeping her hands warm in a muff—

maybe from an adolescent pelt shot by Clark Gable on a safari

or I dreamed I partied at the White House.

In my own hand-sewn faux-spotted Jackie jacket and pillbox,

I sat with my hubby-to-be in the cheap seats of a gymnasium

to hear Louis Armstrong. He could have been more than fifty,

I only saw meteors spark off his awesome cuff links.

The All-Stars looked suave, like they had manners, could

hold their liquor. As they played, hundreds of heads bobbed.

I guess those tunes blistered Elvis lovers or got to Mama Lucy

in some bones even before an archaeologist said so.

Hubby-to-be said, You go ahead, when I pleaded for company

in the long line of fans waiting for autographs and a starched

handkerchief, of which there were stacks. Once at the table,

Louis growled silky, Baby, there are plenty more in the back.

In that moment of his diamond glance, or was it a Santa wink,

an avalanche of mute escapees left my tongue dry, helpless

in the quandary. I was awhirl in the curlicues of his name

walking the baseline stripe to the exit.

It would be another winter before I rode trolleys in New Orleans.

On the way, I'd see bullet holes in the walls of Jackson State.

Hubby-to-be number two took me to Marie Laveau's grave.

I now keep a wad of hair from men I've known who adore the trumpet.

Some of these bootleggers,
they make pretty good stuff;
Plenty of places to hide
things here if you want to
hide 'em bad enough.

—Bob Dylan,
"Sugar Baby" (2001)

SHADOW PLAY:
B-C-D
AND BACK
{ By Robert Polito }

There is the kick of the illicit—and the rarer kick of illicit *knowledge*. Bootleg recordings embody both. You tell yourself as you depart the site of purchase, I am not meant to have this; and later, as you listen alone in your apartment, I was not meant to hear—overhear?—it.

★ ★ ★ ★

No one would care about the shadow career of Bob Dylan if his official albums weren't so conspicuously innovative and legendary. But **Premise B:** What if Dylan's illicit recordings—bootlegs of live performances, studio outtakes, rehearsals, and unreleased songs—ultimately prove, as now appears likely, his most vital, revelatory, and enduring work?

Since 1962 Dylan has released some forty-plus albums of new music, mainly on the Columbia or Sony/Columbia label, yet on any given afternoon around Greenwich Village there is a variable stock of Dylan bootleg CDs roughly five to ten times the span of his official catalog. Commercial but unlicensed, bootlegs travel an underground though scarcely clandestine

{ **Alongside the popular Dylan legend of masterpieces and betrayals, I wish to posit an entire parallel ghost world of once and future bootlegs.** }

B
C
B
C
D
D

economy along the outskirts of fandom. Bootlegs aren't pirate recordings—counterfeit copies of lawful goods—just as bootleg stores aren't really haunts of Bob collectors, a still more crepuscular if arguably "purer" network of swapped cassettes and archival pages of the young Dylan's marginalia in Woody Guthrie's *Bound for Glory*.

Bootlegs once flaunted mimeographed sleeves, and vinyl that visibly degenerated during play. Now the moonshine tops the official releases in style and authority—meticulous annotation, lavish booklets, often stunning sound, and smart titles: *Violence of a Summer's Dream*, *The Lonely Graveyard of My Mind*, *After the Crash*, *Stuck Inside New York*, and *Boots of Spanish Treasure*. Paul Williams vividly refocused Dylan as "foremost a performing artist, as

tacular five-CD bootleg set of 103 songs, *The Genuine Basement Tapes*.

Alongside the popular Dylan legend of masterpieces and betrayals, I wish to posit an entire parallel ghost world of once and future bootlegs. Some shadow releases inevitably circle his catalog like spectral moons, restoring songs and brilliant alternate takes to *The Freewheelin' Bob Dylan* (1963), *Blood on the Tracks* (1975), *Infidels* (1983), and *Oh Mercy* (1989) or capturing sharper, more decisive concerts from the tours documented on his official live albums. When Sony/Columbia finally issued *Live 1966: The "Royal Albert Hall" Concert*, in 1998, bootleggers matched and raised it—first in an eight-CD box of coruscating 1966 shows and, then, in a twenty-six-CD box of all extant 1966 concerts from America, Australia, and

---

Bootlegs once flaunted mimeographed sleeves, and vinyl visibly degenerated during play. Now the moonshine tops the official releases in style and authority.

---

opposed to a composer or songwriter" for three books that venture to map the forty years of live shows that comprise the vast terra incognita of Dylan bootleg CDs. Greil Marcus rooted his plangent vision of the "old, weird America" of Harry Smith, Dock Boggs, and Bob Dylan not in the 1975 Columbia collection of sixteen tracks on *The Basement Tapes* but in a spec-

Europe. Dylan's own generous retrospective compendium of studio and live rarities, *The Bootleg Series Volumes 1-3* (1991), prompted the phantom rival of a trio of three-CD packages, *The Genuine Bootleg Series*—a chronological anthology of 157 additional "lost" performances.

But many imposing Dylan shadows find only faint echo in the official chronicle. The sweeter, tent-show-caravan swing of the 1975 Rolling Thunder Revue can be recovered only on wildcat recordings that catch perhaps Dylan's most resourceful singing. Or the gospel music of 1980 and 1981—again illicit CDs, including a Toronto show recorded by Columbia, yield sole entrée to these nuanced, adventurous performances, and to important songs, such as "Caribbean Wind," "Let's Keep It Between Us," or "Yonder Comes Sin," that never reached his albums.

Recently, *Love and Theft* (2001) offered as a bonus track a 1961 Minneapolis version of an early Dylan original, "I Was Young When I Left Home." But the surest guide to Bob Dylan before *Bob Dylan* (1962) are some fragmentary, surreal boots—starting with a 1958 wire-recorder home tape of the Hollywood Flames' "Buzz, Buzz, Buzz," and Little Richard's "Jenny, Jenny," among other songs and conversation ("When you hear a good rhythm-and-blues song, chills go up your spine," he tells his high school buddy John Bucklen), and continuing on a 1960 tape recorded in a St. Paul apartment that reveals Dylan singing a folk repertoire in a charming lilt reminiscent of Elvis Presley's *Sun Sessions* ("He reminded me of a little choirboy . . . with this beautiful voice," an old friend remembers on an accompanying interview track).

Out of the recesses of hotel, radio, and club recordings, Dylan's early engagement of folk and blues in Minnesota, and soon after in New York, emerges as deeper and more various than even all the death-haunted songs on Dylan's official debut intimate. Traditional tunes frame and ground his live shows into this century. The fearsome *Golden Vanity*, for instance, sweeps up a grievous parade of old ballads culled from late-eighties and early-nineties tours, only one song reappearing on his official folk collections, *Good As I Been to You* (1992) and *World Gone Wrong* (1993). Dylan still tends to open shows with traditional covers—often now of the Stanley Brothers, one of the ghost bands in his ongoing shadow play.

Dylan's current concerts (along the self-styled "Never Ending Tour," nonstop from 1988 through the present at a clip of 115 shows a year) so far lack official documentation. Over the past decade, but particularly on his 2000 British and American tours, Dylan steadily staked his claim to the vast inheritance of American music—not only through traditional covers, but also inside nightly recasting of his old and new songs. Nearly all these shows are retrievable on CDs lifted from vivid source tapes. They are fluid summations sustained by his most versatile and sympathetic backing band ever and his own idiosyncratic lead guitar. Dylan's transformation of his catalog over a single evening can summon American music from the earliest anonymous folk airs through the last century of blues, country, gospel, bluegrass, into rock and roll, punk, even heavy metal (a 1994 "Maggie's Farm" invoked "Smoke on the Water"). Although he rarely rewrites lyrics, his modulations of intonation and phrasing might shift a song's meaning utterly: "The Times They Are A-Changin'," for instance, now conjures the end of the world.

During a recent interview in the *Los Angeles Times*, Dylan remarked that he had experienced a creative resurgence in "the early '90s when I escaped the organized media. They let me be. They considered me irrelevant, which was the best thing that could have happened to me." Dylan probably is more visible now in media culture than at any moment since the late 1960s, but his point is that **Premise C:** once outside his official past, free of the ordeal of generation-spokesman, Dylan could luxuriate in another, more resonant myth—his mastery of all-American music.

Throughout his prior official career, every evolution was a variation on New-

port 1965: any fresh move he made, rock, or country, or gospel, marked either a breach of faith ("Judas," as the man shouted at Manchester in 1966) or a return to the fold ("We've got Dylan back again," as *Rolling Stone* intoned in 1970). *That* Dylan was the Byron of his era—yet as an innovator inside a musical tradition, he stands closer to Louis Armstrong, and as a singer inhabiting a lyric, he is nearer Sinatra.

His current shows can converge and reinvent songs from any year: *Slow Train Coming* (1979) and *Nashville Skyline* (1969) alongside *Highway 61 Revisited* (1965), *Blonde On Blonde* (1966), and *Blood on the Tracks* (1975); *Bob Dylan* (1962) and *Freewheelin'* (1963) next to *Infidels* (1984), *Oh Mercy* (1989), and *Time out of Mind* (1997). His shadow world in that sense is timeless. Released from his chronology and history, his songs are all Dylan songs.

Once there were only his official albums—now the shadows heap them.

★ ★ ★ ★

Sometime during the 1970s I lost touch with Dylan's official career, and even now

---

Free of the ordeal of generation-spokesman, Dylan could luxuriate in another, more resonant myth—his mastery of all-American music.

I am more likely to play a bootleg than one of the Columbia albums, unless that recording appeared after I started listening again in 1991. This indifference followed a conventional fascination with Dylan—conventional, at least, for 1960s school*boys*—and was due to **Counterpremise D:** my own conservatism, although I obsessively tracked new music, Bowie, Roxy Music, punk imports, and read about still more records in the English music weeklies. I marveled at Bryan Ferry's elegant tweaking of Dylan on his theatrical cover of "A Hard Rain's A-Gonna Fall" on *These Foolish Things*, a sly pop art readymade that positioned Dylan alongside Lesley Gore.

Watching the September 1976 NBC broadcast of the Rolling Thunder Revue performing at a rainy Fort Collins stadium, I could lodge only the bewildering differences—in the singing, songwriting, even the gypsy headgear—from the sixties. Not until two decades later when I purchased a bootleg videotape of *Hard Rain*, at a store on Eighth Street, could I recognize the ravishing fury of Dylan's vocal, or the intimations of punk (a few months after the Ramones' debut) particularly in the *Blood on the Tracks* songs: a feral, back-to-the-wall execution of "Idiot Wind."

On occasions when I inadvertently heard Dylan's latest records at parties and dinners, I wouldn't listen also for all the

Counterpremise D: piety. My graduate-school and young poet friends are readily caricatured; my "Byron of his era" line above is an approximation. But by the 1980s, official Dylan—not so much his songs, but the talk around them, and the gnomic recitation of lyrics—seemed nostalgic, self-congratulatory, middlebrow. Dylan famously introduced literature and art to rock and roll, along with pretension and the notion of the masterpiece, what Manny Farber, writing of film, once tagged "the square, boxed-in shape and gemlike inertia of an old, densely wrought European masterpiece." Yet the masterwork **Premise C:** couldn't be more inimical to his shadow enterprise.

Two events from 1991, only fitfully linked, focused this Dylan ghost world. On February 20 Dylan accepted a lifetime-achievement award at the Grammy Awards in New York. This was the eve of the Gulf War. Although pressured to reprise "Blowin' in the Wind" for the troops, he elected instead the sardonic "Masters of War"—except Dylan looked a sodden mess, and he chanted the words in an indistinct blur. He followed the song with a short, halting speech of nearly Napoleonic self-loathing:"My daddy once said to me . . . he said, 'Son . . . it is possible for you to become so defiled in this world that your own mother and father will abandon you . . . and if that happens, God will always believe in your ability to

His hesitations, second-guesses, and revisions enhance the story.

mend your own ways"....Thank you." The moment, as they say, caught your attention, and five weeks later Columbia issued *The Bootleg Series Volumes 1-3*, the collection that started to reconfigure the past Dylan seemed to be running away from, and which was running away with him.

A chronological survey of thirty years of rare and unreleased songs, this imitation black-market CD box charted an alternative recording career for Dylan, salvaging jettisoned wonders, such as "Angelina," "Foot of Pride," and "Blind Willie McTell." There was the hint of a different artist, tentative, experimental, alert to accident, captivated by process, and a hint, too, of all the other missing songs that would soon turn up—are still turning up—on hundreds more shadow CDs. Not long after, I sought out my first bootleg on Thompson Street, a live recording from 1981 titled, prophetically, *Stadiums of the Damned*.

Dylan's official history is haunted by the masterpiece, every strong new record acclaimed his best since (choose one) *Blonde on Blonde*, *Blood On the Tracks*, or *Oh Mercy*. But ghost collections of studio outtakes impart an interactive spirit to his albums—what if this or that track is restored to, say, *Infidels*—much as concert bootlegs indicate that no song is finished, no take definitive. *Blood on the Tracks* probably is, as Rick Moody suggested at the PEN Town Hall sixtieth-birthday tribute, the most complete and honest account of a love affair ever recorded. Yet the emotional arc is more poignant after you hear the original New York versions of "Idiot Wind," "Tangled Up in Blue," "If You See Her, Say Hello," and "You're a Big Girl Now"—and still more devastating after you listen to Dylan reimagine the songs over twenty-five years of live shows. His hesitations, second-guesses, and revisions enhance the story: a truculent 1976 "Shelter from the Storm" that denies all refuge, and a distant, elegiac 2000 version, tendered like a fable from a previous life.

To my 1980s friends, Dylan was a sage who disguised all the answers—the shadow singer of the bootlegs is nothing but questions.

* * * *

Bob Dylan betrays the disconcerting sensation that **Premise B:** He dwells inside a private landscape of the great dead. These posthumous conversations span such monuments as Robert Johnson, Jimmie Rodgers, Hank Williams, Son House, Woody Guthrie, Blind Willie McTell, and Charley Patton, and marginally slighter markers on the order of Sleepy John Estes, Skip James, Rabbit Brown, Mance Lipscomb, Jesse Fuller, John Lee Hooker, Bill and Charlie Monroe, Buell Kazee, Emmett Miller, and Frank Hutchison. "They weren't there to see the end of the traditional people," Dylan once remarked of younger folk musicians. "But I was." Inside this landscape, the occasional live emissary, such as Ralph Stanley, also seems like a revenant.

Beyond a plausible spread of blues, rockabilly, and bluegrass covers, ranging from the Stanleys to Muddy Waters and Elizabeth Cotton, Dylan can direct his band past some inconceivable vistas— Charles Aznavour ("The Times We've Known") and Dean Martin ("Return to Me") among them. At Frank Sinatra's 1995 eightieth-birthday celebration, the strings on Dylan's arrangement of "Restless Farewell" hovered arrestingly between country swing and Nelson Riddle. During recent circuits of the Never Ending Tour he revamped songs from *Time out of Mind*, layering them with echoes of Hoagy Carmichael and Charley Christian. *Love and Theft* revisits an instant in the late 1920s when country, blues, jazz, and minstrelsy improbably merged, before resuming discrete paths.

"I find the religiosity and philosophy in the music," Dylan told David Gates in *Newsweek*. "I don't find it anywhere else. Songs like 'Let Me Rest on a Peaceful Mountain' or 'I Saw the Light'—that's my religion. I don't adhere to rabbis, preachers, evangelists, all of that. I've learned more from the songs than I've learned from any of this kind of entity. **Premise C:** The songs are my lexicon. I believe the songs."

★ ★ ★ ★

The first Dylan (and the first rock) bootleg, the vinyl *Great White Wonder* of 1969, a farrago of basement songs and Minneapolis home sessions, originated in a critique of the songwriter that implied he either had lost his way or no longer could recognize his strongest work. "DYLAN'S BASEMENT TAPE SHOULD BE RELEASED," as the headline ran in *Rolling Stone* for a cover story, "THE MISSING BOB

"They weren't there to see the end of the traditional people," Dylan once remarked of younger folk musicians.

Just days after I sat down to write, Counterpremise C: federal agents raided four stores in Greenwich Village, seizing every bootleg CD on the premises.

DYLAN ALBUM." He was muddying a once-clear picture with strange new music, and bootleggers knew best. Slipped inside *Great White Wonder* was **Counterpremise D:** a sentimental conjecture (which this Shadow Play cannot fully escape) that somewhere else—back into the past, or on a secret tape—"the real Dylan" endures. Oddly, though, now **Premise D:** the only angle where a reductive search for a truer Dylan vanishes is on the bootlegs: over the sweep and reach of his shadow recordings he is, of course, everywhere, and nowhere.

Dylan's own attitude toward the ghost world is predictably double. Even as in interviews he scolds "those folks out there who are obsessed with finding every scrap of paper I've ever written on, every single outtake . . . It's called stealing," Columbia/Sony teases obsessives with rarities, and his Web site (bobdylan.com) circulates live songs. And every dealer I've ever met tells a story of Dylan exclaiming over some stylish contraband, "Hey, these guys do a better job than my label!"

Just days after I sat down to write, **Counterpremise C:** federal agents raided four stores in Greenwich Village, seizing every bootleg CD on the premises. Past busts tended to interrupt, though not stop, the weekly influx of fresh titles, but so far only legit product sits in the racks. The agents ignored a few smaller outlets that more cleverly and confusingly mix boots among imports; still, the nervous owners relegated the moonshine to the back room.

Then the twin towers came down. When lower Manhattan opened again I walked by the raided shops—the grates were up, yet there was nothing for sale you couldn't buy at Tower.

But around the corner, inside a little store they missed, my friend Richard was setting out his stock as before.

"I'm guessing," he said, "that **Premise B:** the FBI has bigger things on its mind right now." ▮

The agents ignored a few smaller outlets that more cleverly and confusingly mix boots among imports.

The Old Record

— by —

Sean Singer

rolled out   of the hot machine

     the Scully Automated Lathe,

         covered in   oil,

rigged to the metal   ends,

             dying of spin,

metal   on black,

       back-to-back thimble weights, diamond

          and rinsed

     to a new shine,

lunge and pull into   circles,

      100 grooves to the centimeter,

    calling it vinyl, midnight candle,

     drops onto the place

   with   the   push of the nidifugous chirping needle,

       a bell crank leadplant,

    resting in a red scissor over

          the lumps of steel,

     then rising

with

throstle

smoke,

jazz dust,

rumbly with the blues,

the old rumormonger taking us

to the juke,

(the Bambara word that is

wicked

!)

bouncing resin polymer   lost to the racy sough

of *"Baby she got a phonograph,*

and it won't say a lonesome word

Baby she got a phonograph

and it won't say a lonesome word

What evil have I done

what evil has the poor girl heard?"

THE ENDURING
ART OF THE
PARISIAN SONG

La Chanson
Française

I do not remember who first proposed that all the arts tend toward the condition of music, but I have not heard it gainsaid—the remark touches a chord. Perhaps because by transcending the conceptual level of words and images music reaches us directly through emotion, which is the

by Shusha Guppy

intuitive spring of art. Thus, more than any other art, music is initiatory. Emanating from *Mundus Imaginalis*—William Blake's "The Imaginations"—music initiates us, in our common humanity, to the mysteries of Being.

*N*owhere is this initiatory aspect of music more manifest than when poetry and music unite and give birth to a new entity: song. The charm of the melody facilitates the perception of the poetry while the letter helps the apprehension of the music, and both remain in the mind long after the initial hearing, helping memory to recapture significant moments and feelings.

Of all musical instruments, the most beautiful is the human voice, for it is designed by God. In traditional societies a beautiful voice has always been considered a rare and precious gift, the sign of a special blessing. From the incantations of the Buddhist and Zoroastrian priests through the chanting of Jewish cantors and Christian monks, the melodic call to prayer of the muezzins and the Sufi *sama'* (chant), the singing voice has been at the center of ritual in all spiritual traditions, a bridge between sacred and profane, heaven and earth.

Poets have always known the magic of song. From the day Orpheus picked up his lyre, matched words to the strains of its chords, and created the poetry we call lyric—defined by dictionaries as "poetry that can be sung"—through the medieval troubadours and minstrels to some songwriters of our own time, poets and bards and rhapsodists, major and minor, have poured out their hearts in song, and found echoes in ours. Many are unknown—the varied wealth of folk songs, orally transmitted through generations, attests to the power of song as a conveyor of shared emotion.

I was born and grew up in a traditional Muslim country, in a devout milieu where the chanting of sacred texts and mystic poetry was woven into the texture of daily life. The position of music in Islamic societies is varied, ranging from complete prohibition to total acceptance, with Saudi Arabia and India at either extreme. (A poignant scene in Wilfred Thessinger's classic *Arabian Sands* describes a little boy's hand being chopped off after he is heard singing.) By contrast, many of today's world-famous Indian musicians are Muslim, belonging to patrician families whose musical traditions go back several generations.

It is said that the prejudice against music dates back to the Umayyads, who ruled over the Islamic world from their capital, Damascus, between A.D. 661 and 750. Having espoused Islam reluctantly, the first Umayyad caliphs relinquished the asceticism and unworldly stance of the Prophet and his first followers for a life of luxury and pleasure. They looked to the West and vied with Rome, built grand palaces and established royal courts, drank wine (forbidden in Islam) and employed dancers and musicians. Their women singers and dancers often came from non-Muslim and lower echelons of society, and were none too virtuous. The association of music and dancing with moral laxity can be traced back to their period. But there is nothing in the Holy Koran that prohibits either music or singing. On the contrary, there are hadiths—prophetic traditions—that point to the appreciation of singing. "You must sing the Koran with a sad voice, for it has come with sorrow," the Prophet is quoted saying (the reference is to the sorrow of God for the plight of man and the sufferings of his prophets). "Two people must be

In traditional societies a beautiful voice has always been considered a rare and precious gift, the sign of a special blessing.

especially thankful to God: those endowed with beautiful eyes and those with beautiful voices," is another hadith.

In our house there was no music. Yet my first musical memories are of the sound of my father's voice chanting the Koran in the night, and the singing of mystic poetry by his students who came to visit. Persian music is modal, which allows a good deal of vocal arabesques and embellishments, and adapts easily to the rhythms of poetry. There is no poem, from the *Ghazals* of Hafiz to the quatrains of Omar Khayyam, which cannot be sung on one of the musical modes, while the *Mathnavi*, the mystical poems of thirteenth century poet Rumi—now so fashionable as to be Madonna's favorite poet—are sung with an original melody of the same name. My father, a philosopher who taught at the University, had a velvety baritone full of pathos, while some of his students were magnificent tenors. They sang the poems of Rumi, Khayyam, Hafiz and other Sufi poets that told of love and passion, the torments of separation and the ecstasy of union with the Beloved. Their crystalline voices filled the house, and everyone stopped to listen in rapt attention. Famous classical singers of the time sang exactly the same poems with the same tunes, only accompanied by Persian instruments—*tar, santour, donbak, kamancheh* (variations of zithers, string instruments, and hand drums)—and in public, but their activity was frowned upon and their social status considered inferior. Why, I wondered? Even as a child I was puzzled by the discrimination.

At any rate, singing was confined to men, as women were not allowed to chant their prayers or the Koran—they murmured them sotto voce. Only once did I hear my mother sing a line of a lullaby she recalled from long ago—her voice was rich and sweet, and I wanted more, but she was so devout that she bit her lip for even that small transgression. As for professional women singers, great artists and adored by the public, they were considered beyond the pale. "A woman who sings should have her tongue cut out" went the saying.

I sang. It came as naturally as speech, and at almost the same time. I was sent to the first and only Western-style nursery school, opened in the 1930s after the abolition of the veil and the beginning of women's liberation. We were taught songs, and the teacher "discovered" my voice. I was encouraged, and I soon learned that singing was an act of propitiation, of deflecting hostility and provoking affection. There was no stopping me, yet I was stopped: after the age of twelve I was not allowed to sing in public lest my reputation—and the chance of a good marriage—be impaired. But I sang in private gatherings, among friends.

My source of songs was the radio. When radio came to Persia, the more westernized and progressive households acquired one immediately, but it took years for it to come to our house, and even then it was switched on only for the news and the *Azan* (the muezzin's call to prayer) at noon and the chanting of the Koran at sunset. But I had a westernized uncle, who lived nearby

> There was no stopping me, yet I was stopped: after the age of twelve I was not allowed to sing in public lest my reputation—and the chance of a good marriage—be impaired.

with my grandmother and aunt, and he had a radio, a prewar model in the shape of a bell jar, with a speaker in the middle. At first my grandmother thought that there was a jinn in the box who produced the sounds and voices, but after explanation she decreed that man was indeed as fiendishly clever as the devil himself. Live concerts of Persian classical music were transmitted in the evening and I seldom heard them, but during the day they often played records of Western music, including an hour of French chansons. I was enthralled, and without understanding a word of French I learned them by heart, and I sang them at school and parties to great appreciation. The French chanson, transmitted in its ravishing variety through the mellifluous voices of Tino Rossi, Charles Trenet, and Danièle Darieux on their old records, became my first love, the gateway to my adolescent dreams of love, romance, adventure, freedom. I never thought that decades later I would sing and record the same songs, now revived and recorded by many contemporary singers. I resolved to learn French and go to Paris, where all these idols lived and everything was possible.

*T*he history of the chanson goes back nearly a thousand years to the Crusades and the troubadours. Influenced by the love poetry of the Arabs that was brought back by the Crusaders, the troubadours of Provence—their name derives from *trobar*, to invent, to find—invented new melodies and rhythms, and sang their songs accompanied by their own instruments, principally the lute. They went from castle to castle singing their love songs in the vernacular *langue d'Oc*. Their influence spread to the rest of France—their counterparts in the north were called trouvères and sang in the *langue l'Oïl*.

The troubadours and trouvères exalted the Feminine: their chanson was the key to the *jardin clos*—"enclosed garden"—of the beloved entrusted to the human voice. They promoted *l'amour courtois*—courtly love—which did not seek physical fulfillment, only permission to worship and celebrate the *dame*. They influenced all European lyric poetry. One of the most famous troubadours was Guillaume d'Aquitaine, who is said to have inspired Gerard de Nerval's *El Destichado*:

Je suis le ténébreux, le veuf, l'inconsolé.
Le Prince d'Aquitaine à la tour abolie:
Ma seule étoile est morte et mon lute
    constellé
Chante le soleil noir de la mélancholie . . .

(I am the brooding shadow—the
    bereaved—the unconsoled
Aquitaine's Prince of the doomed
    tower:

My only star is dead and my astral lute
Bears the black sun of melancholy)
—Translated by William Stone, 1999

The troubadours flourished from the eleventh to the thirteenth centuries, then faded, but the tradition of the chanson—poetic song—that they established has endured to this day.

French poets who followed the troubadours used to sing their poems—Rutebeuf, a thirteenth-century trouvère poet, sang his *complaintes*; François Villon, the first of the great French lyric poets, who escaped hanging several times, sang his *ballades*—among them *La Ballade des Pendue*, his best-known poem. Later the poets of the *Plaïades* Pierre Ronsard (1524-95) and Joachim du Bellay (1522-60) used to sing their poems and accompany themselves on the lute. They say that in the sixteenth century in Lyon, the ravishing Louise Labé (1524-66), one of France's greatest poets, gave soirées at which her marvelous sonnets were performed by professional singers.

In England too, from Shakespeare to William Blake, poets sang their own songs. Some of Blake's early poems, written between the ages of fourteen and sixteen, bear the title of "Song." He used to improvise melodies for them; some have a feminine voice:

My silks and fine arrays,

My smiles and languished air,
By Love are driv'n away,
And mournful lean despair,
Brings me yew to deck my grave,
Such and true lovers have . . .

In Paris I was a student at the university, but I also sang. I loved *la chanson Française,* the French chanson, in all its rich variety. It seems to me that it is the most delicate and refined expression of French genius, equivalent to the Persian miniature, the art of flower arrangement in Japan, or jade carving in China. It is part of the fabric of community beyond social stratification or age.

Some consider the chanson a minor form of poetry. I do not believe in such hierarchical divisions in the arts. A beautiful song satisfies two elemental human needs: for poetry and for music. It is quintessential, distilled, like a solitaire diamond, or a drop of tear.

*I*n the cultural effervescence of postwar Paris, the chanson flourished. Chansonniers (singer/songwriters) such as Jacques Brel, Georges Brassens, Léo Ferré, Anne Sylvestre, and Barbara produced memorable chansons, which Juliette Gréco, Yves Montand, and others turned into popular hits. (Edith Piaf belonged to the prewar generation.) Poems by Louis Aragon, Paul Eluard, Jacques Prévert, and lesser poets of the day were turned into chansons by composers to popular acclaim. Jacques Prévert's "Les Feuilles Mortes," put to music by Joseph Kosma, became a universal hit and has remained a favorite of *chansonniers* to this day; the same goes for Jacques Brel's "Ne Me Quitte Pas"—each generation discovers them anew. So popular were Jacques Prévert and Joseph Kosma's chansons that decades later Serge Gainsbourg wrote a nostalgic song about his youth during the fifties entitled "La Chanson de Prévert," which became a hit with the young

It seems to me that it is the most delicate and refined expression of French genius, equivalent to the Persian miniature, the art of flower arrangement in Japan, or jade carving in China.

trouvères by eschewing orchestras and singing to the accompaniment of their own instruments, in tiny *boîtes*—nightclubs— in St.-Germain-des-Prés, of which the most famous was Le Tabou, where Gréco sang. By the time I reached Paris they had all become stars and left the Left Bank clubs for large concert halls and big tours. Le Tabou had closed down, but I went to L'Echelle de Jacob, a tiny hole-in-the-wall in Rue Jacob, where Brel had appeared every night, and heard other singers, perched on their stools, hunched over their guitars, singing

who were not even born then. Even Jean-Paul Sartre, moved by Gréco's deep, dark voice, wrote a song for her: "Le Rue des Blancs Manteaux"—something about scaffolds being erected in the street. It was not very good, and he did not try again. But Antoine Roquentin, the protagonist of *Le Nausée*, finds existence bearable only when he listens to the voice of a black American singer.

Brel, Ferré, Sylvestre, and their followers harked back to the troubadours and

their songs. Some became famous in their turn. (Years later I recorded Brel's "Song of Old Lovers" in my English version on my first record in England.) At the nearby club L'Écluse I heard Barbara on her debut engagement. She too would soon take her place in the firmament, to be seen from afar at the Olympia, Paris's huge concert hall.

At L'Abbay, a small club in St. Germain, two Americans, the African-American actor Gordon Heath and his friend

Lee Payant, sang American and English folk songs accompanied by their own guitars:

> Black, black, black
> Is the color of my true love's hair...

The place was packed every night with Anglo-Saxon expatriates and French admirers. It was the beginning of the folk revival in America and England, and some of their folk songs were played on the radio, sung by a young girl with a pure ravishing voice called Joan Baez.

One evening I went to see an exhibition of collages by Jacques Prévert in an art gallery in St.-Germain-des-Prés. It was late, and the place was empty save for a few young people moving quietly around. The pictures were like Prévert's poems—and chansons—original, inventive, tender, funny, gently irreverent. Ships sailed in the sky toward the moon, angels danced on priests' heads, strange fauna roamed in enchanted woods. A middle-aged man with white hair, a cigarette at the corner of his lips, approached me and introduced himself—Jacques Prévert. I told him that I sang his songs. "I can hear them in your voice," he said, and invited me to go and sing them to him. Months went by before I could summon the courage to ring him.

I arrived with my guitar and sang one of his songs. He called in his wife and daughter to listen, and afterward he picked up the telephone and arranged for me to see the head of a record company. It led to my first record, of Persian love songs, and to our friendship until his death. A year later I left Paris, married an Englishman, and settled in London. By then the cultural centers of the Western world had shifted to the Anglo-Saxon sphere. One aspect of the change was the folk revival of the sixties, the advent of new troubadours and bards such as Bob Dylan, Leonard Cohen, Joni Mitchell, et al. One of the first folk clubs in London was the Troubadour, where Bob Dylan and Paul Simon first appeared. Their songs conquered the world through the resonant

More than anything else, Ted Hughes's encouragement, the songs of Dylan and Cohen, and the voices of Joan Baez and Judy Collins enabled me to write and sing in English.

voices of Joan Baez, Judy Collins, Nina Simone, and countless others.

At a poetry festival in London I sang a couple of songs by William Blake which I had put to music. Ted Hughes was there, reading, and we met. He later sent me a poem, "Water Song," to turn into song. I showed it to Stanley Myers (best known for his "Gavottine," the theme of the film *The Deer Hunter*), and he wrote the music for it and accompanied me on my record. Ted Hughes was generous and wrote a superb piece for the sleeve. The most beautiful, put to music by Stanley Myers, is "Thomas the Rhymer's Song," which I called "When You Are Old Enough to Love." It was on a record of songs by English poets, *Durable Fire*, and I sang it at his memorial service at Westminster Abbey in 1999. More than anything else, Ted Hughes's encouragement, the songs of Dylan and Cohen, and the voices of Joan Baez and Judy Collins enabled me to write and sing in English.

This year Bob Dylan's sixtieth birthday was celebrated with all the fanfare he deserved; Joan Baez is not far off—we are all getting on, and I write prose. But ours was a golden age of the French chanson and its counterparts in America, England,

I sang to the poet on the terrace behind the red wings of the Moulin Rouge.

Ireland. The songs will endure, one hopes, and others will sing them in due course:

Long temps, long temps, long temps,
 après que les poètes ont disparu,
Leurs chansons courent dans les rues . . .
(Long time, long time, long time after
 the poets have disappeared
Their songs will still whirl in the
 streets)
—By Charles Trenet

For me it all began with that chanson of Prévert's, which I sang to the poet on his terrace behind the red wings of the Moulin Rouge all those years ago, and last year at the celebration of his hundredth birthday:

The tide had turned, the sea has
 receded far away,
But you, lying in your sand bed like an
 algae,
Gently caressed by the wind, softly
 move as you dream.
The tide has turned, the sea has
 receded far away,
But in your half-open eyes, two little
 waves have remained—
Enough to drown me.

THE CONTEMPORARY

POP MUSIC
OF AFRICA:
AN APPRECIATION

FROM LEFT: MARGARET PORTER TROUPE, QUINCY TROUPE, AND HUGH MASEKELA, WHO IS PLAYING TO THE GODS UPON HIS FIRST RETURN TO SOUTHERN AFRICA IN MORE THAN 20 YEARS, IN DECEMBER 1980, OUTSIDE MASERU, LESOTHO

209

BY
QUINCY
TROUPE

There was a time not too long ago, that when the subject of African music came up, many people probably thought about spear-carrying, half-naked black men dancing barefoot around a fire in the middle of nowhere and beating thunderously on large or small drums. Of course this image came from Tarzan movies, or others like it, that depicted sub-Saharan African people as savages. Hugh Masekela, the famous South African musician, mocked this image and concept in his 1966 album entitled *The Americanization of Ooga Booga*. By replacing his own name with "ooga booga," Masekela signifies on the concept of becoming "civilized," either in Europe or America, and on the phony "ooga booga" gibberish spoken by sub-Saharan people in Tarzan movies.

These images no longer apply when it comes to defining what contemporary African music is, and what most Africans are about. Today, not only are many Africans acknowledged to be worldly and sophisticated, much of their music is celebrated around the world. In the past few decades, audiences in New York at concerts of African musicians have become increasingly diverse, including not only Africans but also whites, American blacks, Asians, and Latinos. In fact, on July 6, 2001, I picked up the *New York Times*, turned to the Weekend section, and was stunned to find the lead story "African Music Is Here, And It's Now" written by music critic Ben Ratliff. A huge color photo of Djelimady Tounkara, the great guitarist of the legendary Malian pop group the Rail Band (now called the Super Rail Band), accompanied the story. Two smaller photo inserts showed Les Têtes Brulées, a lesser-known group from Cameroon, and Senegal's great singer Youssou N'Dour, now a superstar throughout much of the world, including here in the United States.

Further on in the story there were two other large photos: one of another great Senegalese singer, Baaba Maal (who is well known throughout Africa and the world), and the other an intriguing smaller picture of a Congolese singer I had never heard of, Koffi Olomide. According to Mr. Ratliff, Olomide is the most popular singer in all of Africa today and plays regularly to sold-out stadiums across the African continent that hold upwards of a hundred thousand people. Olomide, Mr. Ratliff reported, is especially beloved by women, because of the way he talk-sings his romantic love songs in a deep, baritone voice.

Listening to African music for over thirty years, I had never heard a peep about Mr. Olomide. I have sung the praises of African music—even, in 1995, writing a story for the *New York Times Magazine* on Salif Keita, the former lead singer of the Rail Band—for many years, mostly to deaf ears. Thirty years ago the problem was that very few Americans were listening to the music, not even most of my friends, because of cultural and language barriers. When the *Times* story greeted me on that Friday last July, I was shocked but happy. Today, an enormous range of African music is sleek and polished, has extraordinary, sophisticated musicians, and is internationally appreciated for its profound melodic lyricism.

There is the soukous music of the Congo and Central Africa; the mbaqanga of South Africa, which also impacts Central African and Congolese music; the juju and Afrobeat of Nigeria; the praise-song, griot, Mbalax, dagan, and thieboudienne rhythms of Senegal; the highlife of Ghana; the chimurenga of Zimbabwe; and the Bambara griot music of Mali. The influence of Cuban and American music is widespread throughout much of Africa. Musicians from Senegal, Nigeria, Mali, Guinea and Congo wear extravagant, vivid costumes at their live concerts and are dynamic, first-rate entertainers.

TODAY, AN ENORMOUS RANGE OF AFRICAN MUSIC IS SLEEK AND POLISHED, HAS EXTRAORDINARY, SOPHISTICATED MUSICIANS, AND IS INTERNATIONALLY APPRECIATED FOR ITS PROFOUND MELODY AND LYRICS.

I first became aware of African music in the 1960s, when I heard the South African Hugh Masekela's "Grazing in the Grass," his former wife Miriam Makeba's "Pata Pata," and "Drums of Passion," by the Nigerian drummer Babatunde Olatunji. The vocal power of their music, especially Masekela's gruff baritone voice and Makeba's unique "click-song" styling was mesmerizing. This was the beginning of a love affair that has endured and grown more passionate over the last thirty years.

In 1972, I went to teach African-American literature at the University of Ghana, in Legon—right outside Accra, the largest city in that West African nation—and then to Lagos University, in Lagos Nigeria. The Ghanaians are a very laid back, relaxed people (like the United Nations' Secretary General Kofi Annan), and their culture reflected this. In Ghana there was little physical violence or killings and public life moved at a leisurely pace. Nigeria was quite different. Lagos is a huge, sprawling, dysfunctional city. I found many Nigerians to be very

aggressive, both men and women. The vehicular traffic of Lagos was called "no go" because it hardly moved, and when it did it was chaotic, full of blaring horns and screaming people. On my first day I got into a fistfight with the cabdriver who drove me to my hotel in a dispute over the fare.

In Ghana I heard first the late, great Fela Ransom Anikulapo Kuti and the still thriving King Sunny Ade in Nigeria. Although I had found highlife music in Ghana very interesting, especially the music of C. K. Mann and the group Hedzoleh Soundz, which came to prominence during the 1970s as Hugh Masekela's band, I found the music of both Fela and Ade much more cutting edge; Fela's music was influenced by American funk and jazz, Ade's by the swirling, hypnotic sound of the pedal steel guitar. As dance music, highlife was initially a blend of European jazz music with traditional rhythms of the Akan and Ga, which are the largest indigenous Ghanaian tribes. Added to this musical concoction was the relaxed vocal-and-guitar-based palm-wine music, which is sung in places where the popular fermented wine is consumed. Later, this mestizo music was deepened with calypso, and later still with American country and western.

The more percussive music of Fela and Ade, both Yorubas from Nigeria (as is Olatunji), was more to my liking. Still, despite the fact that they came from similar ethnic roots, Fela and Ade made strikingly different music. Fela's music, though rooted in the traditional drumming music of the Yoruba, drew much more heavily than Ade's on international trends. Fela came from an aristocratic background and education (he was schooled in England), while Ade was from more humble beginnings (the "King" in his name does not indicate royalty, but that he is the king of the style of music he plays). Fela was very political and outspoken, even in the lyrics of many of his songs, while Ade kept his political views to himself.

Fela played a rhythmic music he called Afrobeat. It owed much to the music of James Brown and Sly and the Family Stone. Brown's plucking, edgy guitars and funky backbeat drum rhythms, locked in place by a deep bass pulse, are all over Fela's music. But so are the funky, horn-led, anthemic grooves of Sly and the Family Stone. Further, the music of both Brown and Sly was infused with political

lyrics, as in Brown's "Say It Loud, I'm Black and I'm Proud" and Sly's "Stand." Both of these songs had a lasting impact on Fela's music and lyrics as did the sound of Olatunji; the confrontational messages of the Last Poets; the improvisational style of American jazz, particularly Miles Davis; and the antiapartheid-infused lyrics and gravelly vocal style of Hugh Masekela. (Fela even confessed to me one day that Masekela was one of his idols, along with James Brown and Miles Davis.)

Fela owned a club called the Shrine, where he played nearly every night when he was at home in Nigeria. A flamboyant, outspoken critic of Nigeria's corrupt politicians, during the 1970s and early '80s Fela was Africa's biggest music star. He was a perfectionist about his music. I was invited to one of his rehearsals in 1972 and when he saw I was doing nothing but sitting around observing the band play, he gave me a metal cowbell and a stick and told me to play it. He believed everybody present must participate in some way. For Fela, music was a spiritual exercise. When he told me I had to play or leave, I was shocked, but I played that cowbell as if my life depended on it.

Fela was treated like royalty by those who lived in and around Lagos. I remember once riding with him in Lagos when we came upon a traffic jam. Not wanting to be late for an appointment, Fela simply told the driver to drive on the sidewalk, where there were only vendors, chickens, and people walking. When the people saw Fela's car coming at them without slowing down they dove into ditches. When Fela's car got to the intersection a traffic policeman came over to see why a car was hurtling up the sidewalk toward him. When he saw it was Fela, he simply waved him through with a smile. I was absolutely stunned, flabbergasted by his action, or non-action. Fela wasn't; he just instructed his driver to keep going. Perhaps a mile or so later, he did the same thing, and then he did it again, and every policeman he encountered would wave him on. To tell you the truth, I was scared to death. I couldn't believe it was happening.

If Fela was a king to himself and many of his countrymen, he was a pariah to many high government officials. The harsh criticism of their greed in his lyrics led to increasing harassment and beatings of him and his mother. In his 1976 song "Zombie," he mocks the orders of a troop commander:

> Zombie no go, unless you tell am to
> go
> Zombie no go stop, unless you tell am
> to stop
> Zombie no go turn, unless you tell am
> to turn
> Zombie no go think, unless you tell
> am to think . . .
> Tell am to go straight—joro-jara-jo

> No brains, no job, no sense—joro-
> jara-jo
> Tell am to go kill—joro-jara-jo
> No brains, no job, no sense—joro-
> jara-jo
> Zombie won't go unless you tell
> him to go
> Zombie won't stop unless you tell
> him to stop
> Zombie won't turn, unless you tell
> him to turn
> Zombie won't think, unless you tell
> him to think . . .
> Tell him go straight—left, right, left
> No brains, no job, no sense—left,
> right, left
> Tell him to go kill—left, right, left
> No brains, no job, no sense—left,
> right, left
> Tell am to go quench—joro-jara-jo
> No brains, no job, no sense—joro-
> jara-jo . . .
> Tell him to go die—left, right, left
> No brains, no job, no sense—left,
> right, left . . .

Fela's mother died from her wounds, and he finally landed in jail. Eventually his home was razed and his club burned to the ground.

King Sunny Ade was another story altogether. He was known and loved for making great music. If he had political disagreements with the Nigerian government, he did not mention them. Like

Fela's, his live concerts were and still are a marvel, with dancers swirling and whirling like apparitions in their blooming clothes. The guitar playing in his band is galvanizing. The hypnotic repetitive rhythms focus your body and attention on the music. Here "surround sound" has true meaning. Ade called his music "juju," a hybrid with roots in Christian hymns, indigenous folk music, and the music accompanying Yoruba religious practices that came to be known in Haiti as voodoo, in Cuba as Santeria, and in Brazil as Condomble. Crucially, Ade added the pedal steel guitar to this musical mix.

ADE CALLED HIS MUSIC "JUJU," A HYBRID WITH ROOTS IN CHRISTIAN HYMNS, INDIGENOUS FOLK MUSIC, AND THE MUSIC ACCOMPANYING YORUBA RELIGIOUS PRACTICES THAT CAME TO BE KNOWN IN HAITI AS VOODOO, IN CUBA AS SANTERIA, AND IN BRAZIL AS CONDOMBLE.

The music of Fela and Ade completely changed my notion of what good African music was supposed to sound like. At first I expected the sound of African instrumental playing to be no different from that which I had grown up listening to in America. A saxophone is supposed to sound like a saxophone, a trumpet a trumpet, and so I wasn' t prepared for the difference in the sound that I heard. When I first heard the horn sections playing in Ghana and Nigeria I was sure they were way out of key. After living in Africa for six months, I realized that the voicing of the horns, in particular the harmonic fusing of saxophone and trumpet, was culturally specific to Africa. Fela utilized a lot of combined saxophone-trumpet voicings in his music that, when I first heard them, made me think the horns were just whining. Later, I heard them as hyenas screaming. Then I understood that this blended, culturally based voice was a truly remarkable, original invention of Africa.

In 1972, though my knowledge of African music was still very limited, music from Senegal, Mali and Zaire was beginning to prick my interest. In 1973, "Soul Makossa," by the very fine Ivory Coast singer and bandleader Manu Dibango, became an international hit and had many in New York City including myself dancing to its insinuating, pulsating rhythms until the wee hours of the morning. But it was not until I traveled to Zaire, in 1974, for the Muhammad Ali-George Foreman fight, that I heard more.

Because of a cut that Foreman suffered in training, the Ali-Foreman fight was

King Sunny Ade, 1983

postponed for weeks, and I ended up staying longer than planned. During that time I went to parties and other celebrations. I even met President Mobutu, the dictator, up close. At one point I witnessed him personally hang a young man for picking an American's pocket. Kinshasa was teeming with secret agents loyal to Mobutu, who chauffeured me and others who had come for the fight around the city.

During that month, many lively bands filled Kinshasa's street corners in celebration of the Ali-Foreman fight. Music was everywhere. It was one of the most celebratory times of my life. I've never had as much joy, as much fun, dancing to these rhythms.

The music of Zaire (today the Republic of Congo), including the late, great guitarist Franco, the influential singer Sam Mangwana, guitarist Dino Vangu, the group Bholen & Bavon Marie-Marie, Tabu Ley Rochereau, Papa Wemba, Thu Zahina, Kanda Bongo Man, Zaiko Langa Langa, Loketo, and a host of other fabulous Zaireans mesmerized me. The brilliance of soukous, which is dance music blended with Cuban rumba rhythms and local strains, was irresistibly seductive. Soukous, which owes much to Afro-Cuban music, is characterized by distinctive high-register playing on the guitar; by a wonderful talk-singing style that ranges over octaves; by the interlocking rhythms and the interplay between the rhythm section and voice; and by the lyrical beauty of the melodies of the songs. I can't begin to tell you how much hearing that music impacted me back in 1974. It was like falling in love. As Joe Zawinul, the renowned keyboardist, Miles Davis alumnus, and co-founder of the legendary fusion group Weather Report, told me about playing with Salif Keita, "I love playing with African musicians, because they play with such spirituality, joy and consistently on such a very high level." Exactly why I love listening to the music.

When I first heard Zairean music live in the clubs of Kinshasa, especially the music of Franco (whose real name was Luambo Francis Makiadi) and Sam Mangwana, it was exhilarating. An incredible guitarist, Franco was the colossus of soukous. From the mid-1980s until his death in 1989, Franco and his OK Jazz Band were the most loved and famous of all African musical groups. In the hands of Franco, soukous became a great river of rhythms. Dancing to that music all night at clubs in Kinshasa was almost like having every molecule of my body taken over by a delicious feeling of sensuality that caused my pelvic area to move itself in deep, almost sexual pleasure. The other great bands I heard in Kinshasa were Zaiko Langa Langa, Dr. Nico's band, Tabu Ley Rochereau, among others.

I returned to New York during the fall of 1974, and I ran around telling anyone who would listen about the brilliance of African music. Of course, most people looked at me as if I was crazy. Hardly anyone took me seriously. Since my Zairean experience I have been back to Africa several times, but the most meaningful visit was when I traveled to Maseru to help produce Hugh Masekela and Miriam Makeba's return concerts in southern Africa, in 1980. That experience gave me the opportunity to hear the wonderful bands from that region (Mozambique, Zimbabwe, and South Africa) who came to Maseru, Lesotho to help celebrate the return of these two South African musical giants, who have sizable audiences in the United States and Europe. In 1980 both had been in exile for over twenty years as a protest against apartheid.

Miriam Makeba is the doyenne of all African music and was the one who almost single-handedly brought the music to an international audience in the 1960s with her hits "The Click Song," "Pata Pata" (which reached number twelve on the American pop charts in 1967), and " 'M' Bube," which are blends of traditional South African ballads, jazz, Western pop, folk, and tribal Xhosa and Zulu elements. Makeba has a rhythmic, haunting, lyrical voice that is equally at home in up-tempo dance songs and love ballads. She was brought to this country by Harry Belafonte in the 1960s; Belafonte also produced her recordings. For a time Makeba lived in America while she was married to Hugh Masekela. Subsequently she moved to Guinea, where she met and was briefly married to Stokely

I RETURNED TO NEW YORK DURING THE FALL OF 1974, AND I RAN AROUND TELLING ANYONE WHO WOULD LISTEN ABOUT THE BRILLIANCE OF AFRICAN MUSIC. OF COURSE, MOST PEOPLE LOOKED AT ME AS IF I WAS CRAZY.

Carmichael, before moving back to South Africa, where she resides today.

If Makeba is the doyenne of African music, the trumpeter and singer Hugh Masekela was its prince after his "Grazing in the Grass" reached number one on the American pop charts in 1968. (Harry Belafonte had also helped Masekela come to the United States from South Africa, in the early 1960s, to attend music school.) He soon made a name for himself on the American music scene with his intriguing blend of American jazz, mbaqanga township music, and lyrical ballads and has recorded countless numbers of albums. He still seems to be going strong today. Like his former wife Makeba, Masekela returned to South Africa in the 1990s after many years in exile.

When I traveled to Lesotho with Makeba and Masekela in December 1980, I heard the mbaqanga music of the black South African townships live for the first time. This bass-heavy, rocking, driving music is a hardened, electrified mixture of an earlier South African music called kwela-marabi, which mixed pennywhistles, Dixieland jazz, the sound of black workers singing in the shabeens (the formerly illegal drinking places for blacks in South Africa), and acoustic guitar. Kwela-marabi was performed by young kids on street corners and became very popular with the crowds who gathered to listen. Mbaqanga also incorporates some western elements, such as blues, rock, the Beatles, the Rolling Stones, and choral singing. Its biggest star, Mahlathini, with his growling, whiskey-soaked bass voice, is almost unknown in the West, but is legendary throughout South Africa. He leads a group called Mahlathini and the Mahotella Queens, who are backed by the Makgona Tsohle Band. One of Mahlathini's biggest rivals for the mbaqanga crown is a group called the Soul Brothers, who also have a very

loyal following in South Africa. Ladysmith Black Mambazo was brought to prominence by performing on Paul Simon's 1987 Graceland tour and on his Grammy-winning album of the same name (Makeba and Masekela also came along and performed on that tour). Mambazo's music reflects the deep influence of African a cappella and American gospel. Thomas Mapfumo, from Zimbabwe (who I hear has recently moved to Portland, Oregon), sings and

Hugh Masekela

composes a music he calls chimurenga, a style that he and his guitarist Jonah Sithole created by transposing mbira rhythms from the thumb piano to guitar. Chimurenga merges songs of the Shono people with lyrics depicting the political struggle Zimbabwean blacks were waging in the late 1970s with whites who dominated the former Rhodesia. The reggae music of Bob Marley has also influenced Mapfumo. Indeed, many musicians who live throughout Africa, have been influenced by Marley's brand of reggae infused with political lyrics.

For sheer musicianship, both Mali and Senegal rival Congo. Salif Keita, Youssou N'Dour, Baaba Maal, Ali Farka Toure, Cheikh Lo, Ismael Lo, and the Super Rail Band are known throughout the world. Much of this region's music is characterized by its use of talking drums—small drums with stretched leather surfaces that are controlled by strings; the drummer holds it under his armpit and pulls on the strings, beating the leather surface with a small stick to create different pitches that come close to a speaking voice—and the stringed kora. The kora produces a sound close to the Western harp and is traditionally used by the singer-storytellers called griots, in whose rituals much of this music has its roots. The music also derives from the wailing prayers chanted by the faithful of Islam. In Senegal, Mbalax, a mixture of traditional talking drums and electric instruments (guitars and synthesizers), is the most dominant musical movement. Its leading practitioner is the amazing singer-songwriter Youssou N'Dour, a mesmerizing performer who sings with a high wailing voice in Wolof, the main indigenous language of Senegal. N'Dour's voice is close in pitch to that of Islamic muezzins when they shout out prayers. He looks like a whirling apparition when he dances, especially if he is wearing the long, white, sheer robe, or bouba, that is indigenous to many parts of Africa. N'Dour is the leader of one of the greatest pop bands in the world. And he is also emerging as one of the continent's most important record producers, producing such stars as Cheikh Lo out of his first-class recording studio outside Dakar.

Although I have not been to Mali, I have heard much of Salif Keita's music live in the United States and Canada. Keita, an albino, has, like N'Dour, a great singing voice. Both singers have wide ranges, covering many octaves, and employ the same high wailing style, although Keita's voice has a penetrating spiritual quality. Although influenced like N'Dour by the sounds of prayer, Keita acquired the eerie power in his voice by shouting monkeys down out of banana trees when he was young. Keita's style is more traditional, closer to that of the griot, than N'Dour's. Both utilize koras, drums, and guitars in their music, but

N'Dour's style is a little more urban and edgy in tone.

Lately, many more women have risen to prominence in African music. In an industry completely dominated by men, this is a welcome and long overdue phenomenon. Singers such as Cesario Evora from Cape Verde; Oumou Sangare of Mali; Deyess Mukangi, Yondo Queen, and M'bilia Bel of Congo; and Angelique Kidjo of Benin have become established stars, following the groundbreaking careers of South African singers Miriam Makeba and her friend Letta Mbulu, who has one of the most distinctive voices in all of African music and reminds me of Aretha Franklin in her range and power.

In many ways the music of Africa has become an interconnected music, first merging with the music of other parts of Africa and then with other regions of the world. With the introduction of recordings, radio, and television throughout the countries of Africa, and especially its urban areas, this process of cross-fertilization has been accelerated. For instance, if you listen closely to the early music of Youssou N'Dour, Baaba Maal, Salif Keita, and many others, you will hear the influence of Fela's Afrobeat and the drum rhythms of Olatunji. Hugh Masekela was profoundly influenced by American gospel, jazz, and the vocal style of Louis Armstrong, and he in turn influenced the singing style of Fela. Ghanaian highlife music owes a large debt to American country and western. Ali Farka Toure, from Mali, has been profoundly influenced by American blues, as his album *Talking Timbuktu*, a collaboration with American guitarist Ry Cooder, aptly demonstrates. And the sponge of African music has also inevitably absorbed rap and hip-hop. Many African fans in certain regions such as Senegal have started demanding that their musical icons play purer, more indigenous music. Thus, Baaba Maal has returned to his griot and kora roots in his latest album, *Missing You*. One thing that I have found common to all African music, especially when the bands perform in their home regions, is that the concerts can be long, perhaps three or four hours, or even longer. This is because it is dance music and people want to dance for hours when they hear it.

The contemporary music of Africa has had a huge influence on other musics in the world, especially in the Caribbean, Latin America, Europe (notably Great Britain), and the United States. Big-name performers such as Paul Simon (especially in his *Graceland* album, which was pro-foundly influenced by South African mbaqanga), the Police and its leader Sting, Peter Gabriel, and the Talking Heads. It was Peter Gabriel who intro-

MANY AFRICAN FANS IN CERTAIN REGIONS SUCH AS SENEGAL HAVE STARTED DEMANDING THAT THEIR MUSICAL ICONS PLAY PURER, MORE INDIGENOUS MUSIC.

duced Youssou N'Dour to a wider audience by including him as a guest singer on his 1987 *So* LP and by involving him on the 1988 Human Rights Now world tour with Sting and Bruce Springsteen. The Talking Heads, influenced both by the novels of the late Nigerian novelist Amos Tutuola and the music of Fela and King Sunny Ade, showed their debt to Fela and Ade on their LPs *Remain in Light* (1980) and *Speaking in Tongues* (1983).

The music even had an influence (along with American jazz, blues, gospel, and rock and roll) on the rhythms and cadences I have incorporated into the language of my poetry. Some African music (along with jazz and blues) has also had a profound impact on the rhythms of another American poet, Jayne Cortez, although her approach is quite different from mine. Cortez actually creates words and sounds that approximate African musical passages, as in the last stanza of her poem, "For the Poets (Christopher Okigbo & Henry Dumas)": "I need kai kai ah i need torn / arms ah / i need canefields ah i need feathers ah i need / skulls ah / i need ashes

blues, snaking horns, where juju grounds down sacred / up in chords, up in the gritty foofoo / magical, where fleet rounds of cadences whirlpool / as in rivers, where memory spins down foaming into dances / like storms swallowed here in a burst of suns / up in the yeasting blue voodoo, holding / the secret clues mum, inside the mystery, unfolding /up in the caking dishrag of daybreak, miracles /shaking out earthquakes of light / like mojo hands luminous with spangling / & are the vamping blood songs of call & response / are the vamping blood songs of call & response."

BOTH CORTEZ AND I ARE INTERESTED IN TRANSPOSING AFRICAN SONG AND DANCE RHYTHMS INTO THE CADENCES EMBEDDED WITHIN THE LANGUAGE OF OUR POETRY. THE DIFFERENCE IS THAT WE EMPLOY DIVERGENT STYLISTIC TECHNIQUES.

ah i need snakes ah i need / eyeballs ah / i need cockroaches ah i need sharkteeth ah I / need buffalo ah / i need / i need spirits ah i need ankles ah i need /hurricanes ah / i need gas pipes ah i need blood pacts ah I / need ah / to make a delta praise for the poets ah."

The rhythms and cadences I incorporate into my poems are not enhanced by neologisms, like Cortez's, but are created altogether by words I select, as in those in the opening stanza of my poem "Avalanche": "within an avalanche of glory hallelujah skybreaks / spraying syllables on the run, spreading / sheets, waving holy sounds, solos sluicing african bound /transformed here in america from voodoo into hoodoo / inside tonguing

Both Cortez and I are interested in transposing African song and dance rhythms (and, I might add, jazz rhythms also) into the cadences embedded within the language of our poetry. The difference is that we employ divergent stylistic techniques in trying to achieve the same poetic result. Also, I might add, we both write from an African—as well as an American—ancestral, cultural memory. This memory resides in most aware African Americans, and it heightens the spiritual impact of listening to African music. It always makes for a very soothing, profound experience for me to hear the music on a daily basis.

REFLECTIONS IN THE MIRROR

I Take a Lot of Pride in What I Am

My Own Kind of Hat

Sing a Family Song

My Life's Been Grand

I've Done It All

Someday We'll Look Back

Love Keeps Hanging On

(Not Till I Was) Old Enough To Fight

Tulare Dust

Grandma Harp

They're Tearing the Labor Camps Down

Hungry Eyes

I Can't Get Away

Driftwood

I Can't Stand Me

Kern River

I'm a White Boy

I Haven't Found Her Yet

Got Lonely Too Early This Morning

Thirty Again

Every Fool Has a Rainbow

Everybody's Had the Blues

Bleachers

Man From Another Time

PRISON

Branded Man

Mama Tried

The Running Kind

My Hands Are Tied

Huntsville

Life in Prison

I Wonder If They Ever Think of Me

Sing Me Back Home

Mama's Prayer

BARROOMS

Swinging Doors

The Bottle Let Me Down

Back to the Barrooms Again

Drink Up and Be Somebody

I Think I'll Just Stay Here and Drink

I Don't Want to Sober Up Tonight

I'll Leave the Bottle on the Bar

Honky Tonk Night Time Man

C.C. Waterback

Wine Take Me Away

Skid Row

Jimmy the Broom

I Wonder Where I'll Find You At Tonight

I Had a Beautiful Time

It's Been a Great Afternoon

Turnin' Off a Memory

I Can't Hold Myself in Line

I Never Go Home Anymore

What Am I Gonna Do (With the Rest
of My Life)

Some of Us Never Learn

Why Am I Drinkin'

Reasons to Quit

I Threw Away the Rose

STORIES AND OBSERVATIONS

Okie From Muskogee

Irma Jackson

The Farmer's Daughter

The Fightin' Side of Me

Big Time Annie's Square

Workin' Man Blues

A Working Man Can't Get Nowhere
Today

Rainbow Stew

Are The Good Times Really Over
(I Wish a Buck Was Still Silver)

If We Make It Through December

Holding Things Together

Daddy Won't Be Home Again for
Christmas

Bobby Wants a Puppy Dog for Christmas

Let's Stop Pretending

1929

The Way It Was in '51

Amber Waves of Grain

The Immigrant

Big City

Shade Tree (Fix-It Man)

The Only Trouble With Me

The Girl Turned Ripe

My Ramona

A Man's Gotta Give Up a Lot

Home Is Where a Kid Grows Up

Billy Overcame His Size

Me and Crippled Soldiers

The Legend of Bonnie and Clyde

Shotgun and a Pistol

Killers Three

All American Cowboy

I Wish Things Were Simple Again

TRAVELIN'

Ramblin' Fever

Silver Wings

Movin' On

Good Old American Guest

No More Trains to Ride

I Won't Give Up My Train

September in Miami

The Seashores of Old Mexico

Red Bandanna

Here in Frisco

Going Where the Lonely Go

Gotta Go See the World

Sky-Bo

Hag's Dixie Blues #2

Old Man From the Mountain

IN THE SPOTLIGHT

Footlights

All I Want to Do Is Sing My Song

No One to Sing For (But the Band)

Please Mr. D.J.

Leonard

Goodbye Lefty

Daddy Frank

White Line Fever

New York City Blues

After Dark

Make-Up and Faded Blue Jeans

There's Somebody Else on Your Mind

This Is the Song We Sing

The Okie From Muskogee's Comin' Home

White Man Singin' the Blues

When My Last Song is Sung

LOVE—LOOKIN'

Always Wanting You

I've Got a Yearning

I Think I'll Stay

If I Could Be Him

Shelly's Winter Love

If You Wanta Be My Woman

Love Will Find You

The Day the Rains Came

Don't Ever Let Your Lover Sleep Alone

Because You Can't Be Mine

Wouldn't That Be Something

Broken Friend

I Just Want to Look at You One More
   Time

Keep Me From Cryin' Today

Shopping For Dresses

Our Paths May Never Cross

LOVE—FOUND

Life's Like Poetry

Today I Started Loving You Again

I Always Get Lucky With You

Twinkle Twinkle Lucky Star

All of Me Belongs to You

You'll Always Be Special

Without You On My Side

Can't Break the Habit

I Didn't Mean to Love You

Don't Seem Like We've Been Together
   All Our Lives

Let's Pretend We're Not Married Tonight

Let's Chase Each Other Around the
   Room

Rose in the Winter

Waitin' on the Good Life to Come

Thank You for Keeping My House

A Shoulder to Cry On

Love Me When You Can

Good Times

After Loving You

My Woman Keeps Lovin' Her Man

Someday We'll Know

Love Don't Hurt Everytime

Susie

The Sunny Side of My Life

Livin' On Your Love

Seeing Eye Dog

These Mem'ries We're Making Tonight

My Favorite Memory

I've Got a Darlin' (For A Wife)

LOVE—LOSING

The Emptiest Arms in the World

Things Aren't Funny Anymore

It's All in the Movies

I'm a Good Loser

I'll Always Know

Look Over Me

I'm Bringin' Home Good News

House of Memories

I'm Gonna Break Every Heart I Can

I Think It's Gone Forever

Whatever Happened to Me

Why Can't I Cry

Chill Factor

Wake Up

I Wonder What She'll Think About
   Me Leaving

I Don't Have Any Love Around

I Forget You Every Day

The Dream

A Place to Fall Apart

My Past Is Present

You Don't Have Very Far To Go

You'll Never Love Me Now

Somewhere Between

Somebody Else You've Known

If I Had Left It Up to You

The Longer You Wait

I'll Look Over You

No More You and Me

Life's Just Not the Way It Used To Be

The Girl Who Made Me Laugh

Am I Standing In Your Way

If You've Got Time (To Say Goodbye)

Mixed Up Mess of a Heart

Nobody Knows I'm Hurtin'

Love and Honor

I Think I'm Gonna Live Forever

For All I Know

A Thousand Lies Ago

Somewhere Down the Line

More Than This Old Heart Can Take

I'm Gonna Paint Me A Bed of Roses

Nothing's Worse Than Losing

I Think I've Found A Way to Live
   Without You

Gone Crazy

Someday When Things Are Good

If You Hated Me

One Sweet Hello

I'd Rather Be Gone

SPIRIT

Thanking the Good Lord

Jesus, Take A Hold

Santa Claus and Popcorn

Goin' Home for Christmas

Grandma's Christmas Card

From Graceland to the Promised Land

Silverthorn Mountain

Don't Give Up On Me

BY EMILY COX AND HENRY RATHVON

ACROSS

1   Shakespeare play containing "solemn and strange music" (3,7)

6   Rhyme scheme, or pop group from Stockholm

9   Muse of music and patron of flute players

10 Author of *A Clockwork Orange* and *Napoleon Symphony*

12 First name in the creation of poetic cantos

13 Author of the novel *The Music of Chance* (4,6)

14 Soprano and actress Lotte

16 Intervals in a major chord

20 Devilish definer of language as "The music with which we charm the serpents guarding another's treasure"

21 Composer of *Camelot* and *My Fair Lady*

24 Greek philosopher who conceived "the harmony of the spheres"

26 Kind of literature delivered by bards and minstrels

28 Bernstein of *West Side Story*

29 French composer of *Suite Bergamasque*

30 Poems of Pindar, Keats, and Neruda

31 Nom de plume of a novelist who loved Chopin (6,4)

DOWN

1   Resonant poem by Edgar Allan Poe (3,5)

2   Recording or writing as in a diary

3   Given name of "Fatha" Hines of jazz

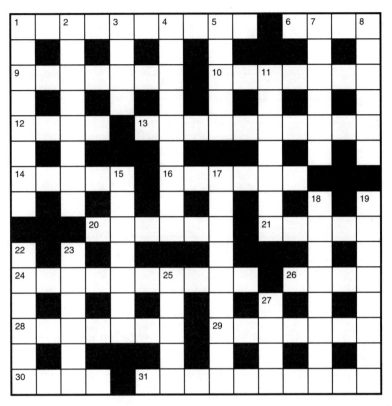

PUZZLE SOLUTION ON PAGE 234

4 Word for a scribbler that is an anagram of "operettas"

5 Female prophet of classical legend

7 Kind of control demonstrated by divas

8 Type of theater typified by *The Bald Soprano*

11 Eleven-line verse form

15 Hero of an Arabian tale (3,4)

17 Compatriot of Snorri Sturluson or Björk

18 Home state of Willa Cather and Fred Astaire

19 Gave a second hearing of an instrument or tape

22 Mythical master of the lyre

23 Irish actor who starred in *Man of La Mancha*

25 Any song from a fondly remembered era

27 Instrument representing the duck in *Peter and the Wolf*

CONTRIBUTORS

A. J. ALBANY is a Hollywood High School dropout. This is her first published work. She lives in a Los Angeles suburb.

NUAR ALSADIR is a poet living in New York.

ZOË ANGLESEY is editor of *Listen Up! Spoken Word Poetry*, and four bilingual anthologies. Her poems have appeared in recent issues of *Manti, Rattapallax, Brilliant Corners, North American Review*, the *Seattle Review*, and *Rattle*. She is a recipient of the W. B. Yeats Second Prize in Poetry. Poetry Editor for the *MultiCultural Review* and jazz, she is also a contributing editor to *BOMB* magazine, including to the "Americas" issue. She teaches a Medgar Evers College CUNY and the New

School University. Forthcoming is *Gazelle Legato*, a volume of poetry.

CLARE CAVANAGH, translator of Adam Zagajewski's poem "Little Waltz", is a professor of Slavic languages at Northwestern University. She has also translated the poetry of Wyslawa Szymborska.

The puzzles of **EMILY COX AND HENRY RATHVON** regularly appear in *Atlantic Monthly*, the *Boston Globe*, the *Wall Street Journal*, and Canada's *National Post*, as well as in *Tin House*. They monitor a crossword chat forum for the *New York Times* on the Web. They live in Hershey, Pennsylvania.

RICHARD EDSON is an actor/musician/photographer. He has appeared in films by

Spike Lee, Jim Jarmusch, Wim Wenders, and Oliver Stone. He was the original drummer for Sonic Youth and has played with Lydia Lunch, Konk, and is currently working with Mr. Razz. His photos have been shown in galleries in Los Angeles and New York.

THOMAS SAYERS ELLIS, the author of *The Good Junk* (Take Three, Graywolf, 1996) and the chapbook *The Genuine Negro Hero* (Kent State University Press, 2001), is an assistant professor of English at Case Western Reserve University and a member of the core faculty at the Bennington Writers Seminars. His work recently appeared in *The Best American Poetry 2001*. The poems in this issue are the first in a series of collaborations between Ellis and P-Funk LP cover artist RONALD "STOZO" EDWARDS. Stay tooned.

DAVID GRUBBS is a Brooklyn-based recording artist and writer. He's originally from Kentucky. His most recent full-length recording is "Act Five, Scene One", which appears on his own Blue Chopsticks label. He recently completed a short radio documentary on Coney Island before and after September 11.

SHUSHA GUPPY is London Editor of the *Paris Review*. She is the author of a memoir, *The Blindfold Horse*. Her essays and interviews have appeared in *Harpers &*

Queen, the *Independent*, and the *Paris Review*, among other publications.

MERLE HAGGARD is a singer, musician, and songwriter.

JUDITH HALL is the author of *To Put the Mouth to* and *Anatomy, Errata: Poems*. She teaches at the California Institute of Technology and serves as poetry editor of the *Antioch Review*.

EDWARD HILL is an Oregon labor lawyer. In previous lives he worked as an ad copy writer, a PR flack, a staff writer for the *Bangkok Post* and *Business in Thailand* magazine, and a stringer for many. He lives in Portland with his wife Holly and their enormous cat Vincent.

ANDREW HULTKRANS is editor in chief of *Bookforum*. A longtime contributor to *Artforum* and *Bookforum*, he has also written on art, film, literature, music, and the media for *Salon*, *Wired*, *21C*, *Filmmaker*, and *Mondo 2000*, where he was managing editor and columnist for three years in the early 1990s.

LAWRENCE JOSEPH'S most recent books are *Lawyerland*, a book of prose, and *Before Our Eyes*, a book of poems, both published by Farrar, Straus & Giroux. A professor of law at St. John's University School of Law, he lives in New York City.

JONATHAN LETHEM lives in Brooklyn and Toronto. His most recent book is *Kafka Americana*.

JULIO MARZÁN is the author of two volumes of poetry: *Translations without Originals* and *Puerta de Tierra*. He is also the author of two books of prose, *The Spanish-American Roots of William Carlos Williams* and *The Numinous Site, The Poetry Of Luis Palés Matos*. He is also the editor-translator of *Selected Poems* by Luis Palés Matos. His poems have appeared in *Americas Review, Parnassus: Poetry in Review*, the *Massachusetts Review*, and *Harpers Magazine*, among others.

RICK MOODY is the author of *The Ice Storm, Purple America, Demonology*, and a forthcoming memoir, *The Black Veil*.

GEOFFREY O'BRIEN is the author, most recently, of *The Browser's Ecstasy: A Meditation on Reading* (Counterpoint Press). He is also the author of *The Times Square Story, Hardboiled America, Dream Time: Chapters from the Sixties*, and *The Phantom Empire*, which was nominated for a National Books Critic Circle Award. *Castaways of the Image Planet*, a collection of his essays on film, will be published by Counterpoint in June 2002. A frequent contributor to the *New York Review of Books*, he lives in New York City.

ROBERT POLITO received the National Book Critics Circle Award for *Savage Art: A Biography of Jim Thompson*. His other books include *Doubles*, and *A Reader's Guide to James Merrill's The Changing Light at Sandover*. He directs the graduate writing program at The New School in New York City.

FRANCINE PROSE is the author of ten novels, including *Bigfoot Dreams, Primitive People, Household Saints*, and, most recently, *Blue Angel*, which was a National Book Award finalist for the year 2000. Her new book, and first book-length work of nonfiction, *The Lives of the Muses*, will be published by HarperCollins in Fall 2002. Her short fiction, which has appeared in such places as the *New Yorker*, the *Atlantic* and the *Paris Review*, is complied in two collections, *Women and Children First* and *The Peaceable Kingdom*. Prose is also a prolific essayist; her nonfiction has appeared in *Tin House*, the *New York Times Magazine, Harper's Magazine* (where she is a contributing editor), *Elle, GQ*, the *Wall Street Journal* and the *New Yorker*. She is the recipient of numerous awards and honors, including Guggenheim and Fulbright fellowships and a PEN translation prize. She lives in New York City.

DAVID RYAN'S fiction has appeared in *BOMB Magazine*, the *Mississippi Review, 5_Trope, Alaska Quarterly Review*, and *Salt Hill*. He lives in New York City.

NINA BERNSTEIN SIMMONS is a writer and filmmaker living in New York.

SEAN SINGER'S poems have appeared in *Pleiades*, *La Petite Zine*, *LIT*, *Slope*, *Callaloo*, *Harvard Review*, *Painted Bride Quarterly*, and *Cross Connect*. He has been awarded a scholarship to the Breadloaf Writers' Conference and an Academy of American Poets prize. His manuscript, *The Golem*, is a finalist for the Yale Younger Poets series. He lives in Cambridge, Massachusetts.

MADISON SMARTT BELL is the author of ten previous works of fiction, most recently the novel *All Souls' Rising*, which was a National Book Award finalist and a finalist for the PEN/Faulkner Award for fiction in 1995. He was recently named one of the Best Young American Novelists under 40 by *Granta*. He lives in Baltimore.

DARCEY STEINKE lives in Brooklyn with her daughter Abbie.

QUINCY TROUPE is the author of thirteen books, including six volumes of poetry, the latest of which are *Avalanche* and *Choruses*, both published by Coffee House Press. He edited *James Baldwin: The Legacy* and is co-author with Miles Davis of *Miles: The Autobiography*, both by Simon and Schuster. His two latest books are *Miles and Me*, a memoir of his relationship with Miles Davis, published in 2000 by the University of California Press, and *Take it to the Hoop, Magic Johnson* (2000), a children's book published by Jump at the Sun, Hyperion Books for Children. In the fall of 2002, Coffee House will publish his *Transcircularities, New and Selected Poems*.

KEN TUCKER is critic-at-large for *Entertainment Weekly*. He also is a music critic for National Public Radio's "Fresh Air."

FREDERICK TURNER'S essay on Henry Miller in Paris appeared in *Tin House's* fifth issue. His imagining of how it might have been when Bix Beiderbecke met Maurice Ravel is from his novel, *1929*.

BILL WADSWORTH'S poems have appeared in the *Paris Review*, the *Yale Review*, the *New Republic*, *Grand Street*, and *The Best American Poetry 1994*, among other publications. He lives in New York City.

ELIOT WEINBERGER'S most recent books are *Karmic Tales*, a collection of essays, and *Unlock*, a translation of the poetry of Bei Dao. He is also the translator of *Nostaligia for Death* by Xavier Villarrutia, which appeared in 1993.

C. K. WILLIAMS' most recent books of poetry are *The Vigil* and *Repair*, which won the Pulitzer Prize, and a collection of his poems on love, *Love About Love*, published in 2001. A book of essays, *Poetry and Consciousness*, appeared in 1998, and a book of autobiographical meditation, *Misgivings*, which received the PEN Marthqa Albrand Award, in 2000. His translation of Euripides' *Bacchae* was performed in 2000 at the 92nd St. "Y" in New York. He teaches at Princeton University.

ADAM ZAGAJEWSKI was born in Lvov, Poland, in 1945. His most recent books include two volumes of poetry, *Canvas* and *Mysticism for Beginners* and two collections of essays, *Two Cities: On Exile, History and the Imagination* and *Another Beauty*, all published by Farrar, Straus and Giroux. *Without End: New and Selected Poems*, which includes "Little Waltz," will appear from FSG in February 2002.

✳ ✳ ✳ SOLUTION FOR PUZZLE ON PAGE 229 ✳ ✳ ✳

CREDITS

EXCERPTS —————————————

P. 132 Geoffrey O'Brien's "Silence in the Age of Noise" is an excerpt from *Jukebox Sonata: Music and Memory in the Recording Era*, which will be published in Fall 2002 by Counterpoint.

P. 154 Frederick Turner's "The Cotton Club" is excerpted from his upcoming *1929: A Novel of the Jazz Age.*

P. 160 "Little Waltz" Excerpted from *Without End: New and Selected Poems* by Adam Zagajewski. Translations by Clare Cavanagh, Renata Gorcynski, Benjamin Ivry, and C. K. Williams. This poem translated by Clare Cavanagh. Published by Farrar, Straus & Giroux Copyright © 2002 by Adam Zagajewski Translation Copyright © 2002 by Farrar, Straus & Giroux. All rights reserved.

P. 223 *Merle Haggard, Poet of the Common Man, the Lyrics* will be published Winter 2002 by Hal Leonard Books.

PHOTOS —————————————

P. 10   *Low Down by A. J. Albany*
        All photos courtesy A. J. Albany
P. 56   *The Music Is by Lawrence Joseph*
P. 56   Aretha Franklin © Corbis
P. 60   Photo courtesy Lawrence Joseph
P. 61   Della Reese © Bettmann/Corbis
P. 62   Count Basie © Bettmann/Corbis
P. 74   Motown Museum © Layne Kennedy Corbis
P. 76   Liner Note illustration by Bill Stanton
P. 109 *Not The Little Boy I Once Knew by*

P. 109 *Andrew Hultkrans*
P. 109 Brian Wilson © Sheeley Gazin/Corbis
P. 117 *Anything Goes by Madison Smartt Bell*
P. 117 Photo collage by Bill Stanton
P 124   *Interview by Francine Prose.*
P 124   Illustration by Bill Stanton
P. 126 Photo courtesy Francine Prose
P. 144 *Far East Side Story by Nina Bernstein Simmons*
P. 149 Bernstein and daughter Jamie, 1962
        © New York Philharmonic Archives
P. 154 *The Cotton Club by Fred Turner*
        Doorman at The Cotton Club
        © Bettman/Corbis
P. 166 *My Guitar by Darcey Steinke*
P. 166 Illustration by Bill Stanton
P. 169 "Guitar" by Pablo Picasso
        © Francis G. Mayer/Corbis
P. 187 *Shadow Play by Robert Polito*
P. 187 & 187 Bob Dylan, 1965
        © Hulton-Deutsch Collection/Corbis
P. 199 *La Chanson Française by Shusha Guppy*
P 199   llustration by Bill Stanton
P. 208 *The Contemporary Popular Music of Africa: An Appreciation by Quincy Troupe*
P. 208- & 209 Photo of Quincy Troupe, Margaret Porter Troupe and Hugh Masekela by Raymond Cajuste © Raymond Cajuste
P. 214 King Sunny Ade 1983
        © Lynn Goldsmith/Corbis
P. 218 Hugh Masekela
        © LynnGoldsmith Corbis
P. 223 *Merle Haggard's Song & Lyrics*
        Faux cover art by Bill Stanton.

this fall

BOOKFORUM

the book review for art, fiction, & culture

on newsstands now

thomas bernhard—a special section
gary indiana and gitta honegger *on* his life and work

jim crace *interviewed by* david l. ulin

luc sante *on* nick tosches

ammiel alcalay *on* charles olson

damon krukowski *on* surrealist painters and poets

lynn crawford *on* mary capanegro

minna proctor *on* susan sontag

john yau *on* javier marias

william monahan *on* *the anatomy of melancholy*

subscribe
2 years 8 issues $16

_____ *Advertise* in Tin House
and Reach Today's Most
Discriminating Literary Audience

"Tin House may very well be the future of literary magazines."
—Village Voice

"Heavy weight and gorgeous."
—Vogue

"It's everything a fine literary magazine should be."
—Willamette Week (Portland, OR)

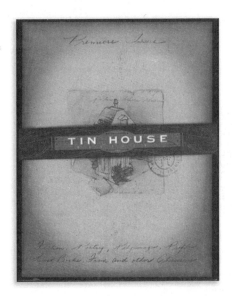

AD RATES

FULL-PAGE
B&W: $400

HALF-PAGE
B&W: $250

Tin House is sold in Barnes & Noble, Borders, and independent newsstands and bookstores across the nation, as well as online at **www.bn.com**

FREQUENCY DISCOUNT: 50% off when you buy four consecutive ads.
——————— Call 503-219-0622 for more information.

Missed
THE FIRST NINE ISSUES?
— Fear not,
we've got a limited number hidden in the closet.

PREMIERE ISSUE: David Foster Wallace, James Kelman, Ron Carlson, Stuart Dybek, Charles Simic, C.K. Williams, Agha Shahid Ali, Rick Moody.

ISSUE 2: David Leavitt, Yasunari Kawabata, Faiz Ahmed Faiz, Quincy Troupe, Les Murray, Seamus Heaney's Beowolf, Walter Kirn, David Gates, Jean Nathan

ISSUE 3: Amy Hempel, Lisa Zeidner, Yehuda Amichai, Sallie Tisdale, and interviews with John Sanford, Mian Mian, and Dawn Powell.

ISSUE 4: Ron Carlson, David Schickler, Aleksandar Hemon, Derek Walcott, Daniel Halpern, Stephanie Mallarmé, Paul West, and an interview with Sherman Alexie.

ISSUE 5: Kevin Canty, Nancy Reisman, Bei Dao, Donald Hall, Jane Hirshfield, Tomaz Salamun, Sylvia Plath, Ann Hood, Patrick McGrath, interview with Ha Jin.

ISSUE 6: The Film Issue, starring Russell Banks, Alex Cox, Todd Haynes, Bruce Wagner, Barney Rosset, Jerry Stahl, Jonathan Lethem, Rachel Resnick, Ann Magnuson.

ISSUE 7: Mary Gaitskill, Lydia Davis, Kathryn Harrison, Nick Tosches, Charles Simic, James Tate, Diane Ackerman, Peter Rock, and an interview with Stanley Kunitz.

ISSUE 8: Elizabeth Tallent, Paul West, Jennifer Egan, Elizabeth Benedict, Jerry Stahl, Josip Novakovich, Billy Collins, Lisa Zeidner, Sallie Tisdale, and an interview with Barney Rosset.

ISSUE 9: Richard Ford, Mary Gaitskill, Jim Shepard, Czeslaw Milosz, David Shields, Mark Doty, Nick Flynn, Diana Abu-Jaber, Paper Doll Cut-Outs, interview with Nancy Milford.

$15 each issue. Make checks payable to Tin House, PO Box 10500, Portland, OR 97296-0500, attn. Back issues.

Stay tuned for issue #11, *due out in April and featuring: Lynn Freed, Marge Piercy, Ron Carlson, Steve Almond, Stuart Dybek, and an interview with Billy Collins.*

Log onto **www.tinhouse.com**

The Yellow Ribbon Snake

a novel
J.R. Dailey

"J.R. Dailey's *The Yellow Ribbon Snake* is a novel that refuses to blink in the face of the pain lives are visited with, and a novel that, without pyrotechnics of any sort, grants the compassion humankind seeks."

—Gordon Weaver
founding editor of *Cimarron Review*

"Dailey writes with the metaphoric passion of Hawthorne and the real-life matter-off-fact edge of Louise Erdrich."

—*ForeWord*

"This first novel is a vividly poignant inside look at the disenfranchised and marginalized people on the fringe of society."

—*Publishers Weekly*

Jacko is a thinking man, but he thinks slowly. He is a big-hearted Vietnam veteran who lives in a homeless camp near a desert truckstop. His sister, Marie, worries about him constantly, when she's not worrying about her relationship with Salazar, a cop, or Rosario, her former boyfriend who deals drugs and carries a gun. Jacko doesn't think he needs Marie's help. She knows he does.

In this gritty, heartfelt novel, people fight and die, secrets are revealed, and souls are redeemed by love.

$12.00, paperback, ISBN 1-880284-37-5
Add $2.50 per order for shipping
California residents add 93¢ sales tax per book

Make check payable to:
John Daniel and Company
Post Office Box 21922
Santa Barbara, CA 93121

Phone orders: 1-800-662-8351
MasterCard, Visa, and American Express accepted

John Daniel and Company, Publishers
www.danielpublishing.com

TIN HOUSE
MAGAZINE

CHECK OUT OUR WEBSITE
www.tinhouse.com

Make yourself at home with the liveliest writing around. Find out how to subscribe, what bookstores carry us, how to submit, and what we are up to in future issues. Sound off, contribute, join a reading group, and check out some of our friendly neighbors.

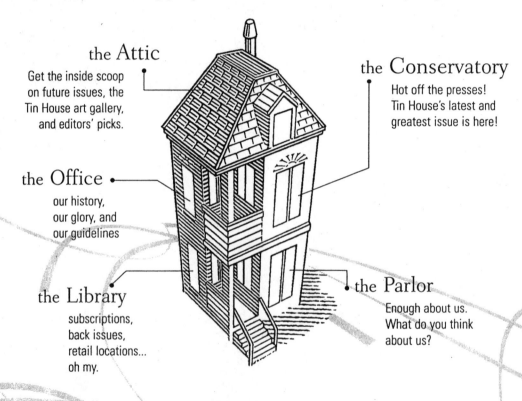

the Attic
Get the inside scoop on future issues, the Tin House art gallery, and editors' picks.

the Conservatory
Hot off the presses! Tin House's latest and greatest issue is here!

the Office
our history, our glory, and our guidelines

the Library
subscriptions, back issues, retail locations... oh my.

the Parlor
Enough about us. What do you think about us?

SNEAK A PEAK AT THE NEXT ISSUE!
including Interviews, Fiction, Poetry, New Voices, and more.

COMING SOON:
The Literary Personals
The Tin House Online Novel